Cognitive Tutor®

Bridge to Algebra

Student Assignments

Early Adopter Edition

 Carnegie Learning®

Carnegie Learning®

Pittsburgh, PA
Phone 888.851.7094
Fax 412.690.2444

www.carnegielearning.com

Acknowledgements

We would like to thank those listed below who helped
to prepare the Cognitive Tutor Student Assignments book:

Ken Labuskes, Author
Marianne O'Connor, Author
Lori Martin, Author
Kent Publishing, Inc.
Signature Design
Michele Covatto
The Carnegie Learning Development Team

ISBN 1-932409-44-0
Student Assignments

Printed in the United States of America
1-2005-VH

Contents

© 2005 Carnegie Learning, Inc.

© 2005 Carnegie Learning, Inc.

© 2005 Carnegie Learning, Inc.

Name _____ Date _____

Money, Money, Who Gets the Money?
Introduction to Picture Algebra

You and your friend Jamal go to lunch. You each order a cheeseburger with everything and a large soft drink. Jamal orders the same, but also orders a small salad, which costs $1.09. The total for both of you is $6.27. How much does each of you owe?

1. Draw and label two "boards" that represent the amounts that you and Jamal owe.

2. Use the picture that you drew to help you solve the problem. What amount does each of you owe? Write your answer using a complete sentence.

Jamal and Carla mow a lawn together to earn some more money for the summer. Carla begins mowing 30 minutes before Jamal. Then they mow together for 75 minutes until they finish. How much time did Jamal and Carla each spend mowing?

3. Draw and label two "boards" that represent the amount of time that Jamal and Carla mowed.

4. Use the picture that you drew to determine the amount of time spent mowing. How much time did Jamal and Carla spend mowing? Write your answer using a complete sentence.

5. What was the total time spent mowing? Write your answer using a complete sentence.

6. Suppose that Jamal and Carla together are paid $15.00. How much were they paid for each hour of work? Remember that 1 hour is equal to 60 minutes. Write your answer using a complete sentence.

7. Because he worked for 75 minutes, Jamal should receive $6.25 of the $15.00. How much should Carla receive? Use complete sentences to explain how you found the answer.

Name _____ Date _____

Collection Connection
Factors and Multiples

1. What factor of 24 is paired with 8? Write all of the factors pairs of 24.

2. What factor of 42 is paired with 6? Write all of the factors of 42.

3. What factor of 35 is paired with 5? Write all of the factors of 35.

4. A collection of 24 marbles is divided into equal-sized groups. What group sizes are possible?

5. Our number system is based on the number 10. The Babylonians based their number system on the number 60. Write all of the factors of 60.

6. Why do you think the Babylonians choose the number 60 as the base of their system? Write your answer using a complete sentence.

7. Lilly listed 1, 2, 3, 4, 8, 12, 24, 32, 48, and 96 as factors of 96. Is her list complete?

8. Caitlin has a collection of CDs. The number of CDs that she has is divisible by 2, 3, 4, 5 and 6. What is the least number of CDs that Caitlin can have in her collection?

9. Write four number sentences using the numbers 3, 6, and 18. Then complete the statements.

    The number 3 is a _____ of 18.

    The number 18 is a _____ of 6.

    The numbers 3 and 6 are a _____ of 18.

Name _____ Date _____

Buns and Dogs
Least Common Multiple

Your club is packing bag lunches for an upcoming trip and wants to include at least one hard-boiled egg in each lunch. There are 8 students going on the trip. Eggs are sold in cartons of one dozen, or 12 eggs. The club wants to put an equal number of eggs in each lunch and have no eggs left over. How many dozen eggs do they need to buy?

1. List the first ten multiples of 8.

2. List the first ten multiples of 12.

3. What numbers are in both sets of multiples?

4. Of the numbers that are in both sets, which is the smallest?

5. How many dozens of eggs does the club need to buy?

In a video game, a character needs to shine a light through two spinning wheels that have holes in them. The first wheel makes a complete rotation in 7 seconds. The second wheel makes a complete rotation in 9 seconds. The holes are lined up at 0 seconds. How many seconds will pass before they are lined up again?

6. List the first ten multiples of 7.

7. List the first ten multiples of 9.

8. What is the least common multiple of 7 and 9? Write a complete sentence to explain your answer.

9. How many seconds will pass before the holes are again lined up?

10. Find the least common multiples of each pair of numbers.

    3 and 5   4 and 6
    8 and 16   10 and 15

© 2005 Carnegie Learning, Inc.

Name _____ Date _____

Kings and Mathematicians
Prime and Composite Numbers

Use the divisibility rules on page 18 in your text to decide whether each number is prime or composite. Use a complete sentence to explain your reasoning.

1. 51

2. 71

3. 45

4. 87

5. 41

All of the prime numbers up to 50 are listed below.

2, 3, 5, 7, 11, 13, 17, 19, 23, 29, 31, 37, 41, 47

6. List all of the even prime numbers.

7. Explain your answer to Question 6 using divisibility rules.

In each list, identify the number that is not prime. Then write a complete sentence that explains why it is not prime.

8. 59, 63, 71, 79

9. 101, 103, 105, 107

Name the property that is illustrated.

10. $27 \times 1 = 27$

11. $2 \times 3 = 3 \times 2$

Assignment

Name _____ Date _____

I Scream for Ice Cream
Prime Factorization

Desmond's class invents a game that they call "Factor It." For each round, the teacher turns over a card with a number on it and the students write a factorization for the number. Students receive 1 point for each factor in their factorization. For example, suppose that the teacher turned over a card with 36 on it.

Desmond writes down 3×12 and receives 2 points.

Cynthia writes down $2 \times 2 \times 9$ and receives 3 points.

Juan writes down $2 \times 2 \times 3 \times 3$ and receives 4 points.

Juan wins the round because he has the most points.

For each number on the cards that the teacher turns over, write a factorization that will get you the greatest number of points in the game. Construct a factor tree to check your answer.

1. 48

2. 72

3. 54

4. 128

5. 640

6. 1000

7. Suppose that the teacher turns over a card that has a 60 on it.
Desmond writes down $(2 \times 2) \times 5 \times 3 = 4 \times 5 \times 3$. Juan writes down $2 \times 2 \times (5 \times 3) = 2 \times 2 \times 15$.
Whose answer is correct? How do you know? Write a complete sentence to explain your reasoning.

Name _____ Date _____

Powers That Be
Powers and Exponents

1. How can divisibility rules help you to find the prime factorization of a 513? Use complete sentences to explain.

For each power, identify the base and the exponent. Then evaluate the power.

2. $6^5 = $ _____

Base:_____

Exponent:_____

3. $1^{12} = $ _____

Base:_____

Exponent:_____

4. $30^2 = $ _____

Base:_____

Exponent:_____

5. $10^4 = $ _____

Base:_____

Exponent:_____

Use a factors tree to find the prime factorization of each number. Then use exponents to write the prime factorization.

6. 40

Prime factorization =

7. 98

Prime factorization =

8. 72

Prime factorization =

9. 128

Prime factorization =

Assignment

Name _____ Date _____

Beads and Baubles
Greatest Common Factor

1. Your aunt's club is planning to sell small bags of different types of beads to people who want to make their own bead jewelry. Below is a table listing the different types of beads and how many they have.

Type of Bead	Quantity
Oval bead	24
Metal bead	18

The club wants to divide these beads into packages so that each package has exactly the same number of oval beads and metal beads. What is the greatest number of packages they can make so that all of the beads are used and there is the same number of each bead in each package? Write your answer using a complete sentence.

1

2. Complete the table to find the greatest common factor of 100 and 64.

Number	Unique Factor Pairs	Unique Factors	Common Factors
100			
64			

The greatest common factor of 100 and 64 is _____.

3. Complete the table to find the greatest common factor of 36 and 48.

Number	Unique Factor Pairs	Unique Factors	Common Factors
36			
48			

The greatest common factor of 46 and 48 is _____.

Find the greatest common factor of each set of numbers.

4. 72 and 30

5. 25 and 50

6. 27 and 80

7. 30 and 54

8. 22, 55, and 110

9. 96, 48, and 80

Name _____ Date _____

Comic Strips
Dividing a Whole into Fractional Parts

Write the fraction that is represented by the fraction model.

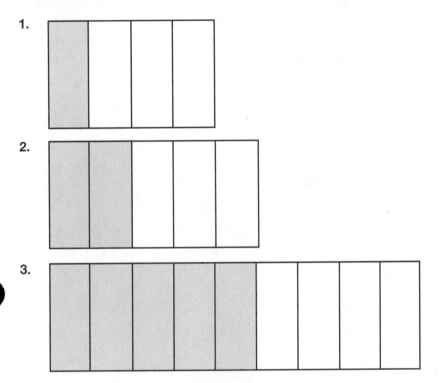

1.

2.

3.

Divide and shade each rectangle to represent the fraction.

4. $\frac{2}{3}$

5. $\frac{3}{5}$

6. $\frac{1}{8}$

7. $\frac{7}{12}$

8. Divide and shade the circle to represent $\frac{3}{8}$.

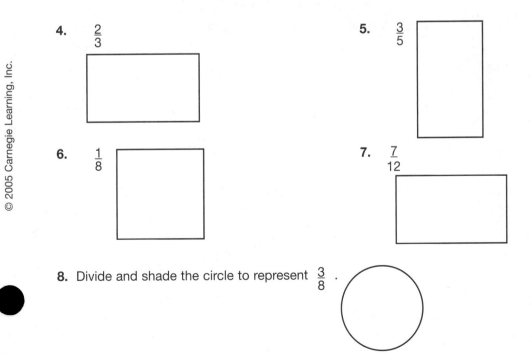

Name _____ Date _____

Dividing Quesadillas
Dividing More than One Whole into Parts

Six friends are sharing 4 quesadillas equally for lunch at a table in the cafeteria.

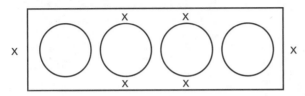

1. Show one way that you can divide the quesadillas equally. How many pieces would each person get? Use complete sentences to explain your reasoning.

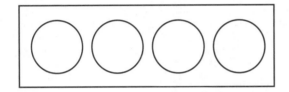

2. Juanita divided all of the quesadillas in thirds. How many pieces would each person get? Write your answer using a complete sentence.

3. Dwayne said he would divide each quesadilla into six pieces. How many pieces would each person get? Is that the same amount of quesadillas that Juanita got? Use a complete sentence to explain your reasoning.

4. Gretchen made 3 pans of lasagna for her 5 friends. Show two different ways can she cut up the pans so that her friends all have an equal amount of lasagna. Draw a picture and explain your solution.

Name _____ Date _____

No "I" in Team
Dividing Groups into Fractional Parts

The swim team is holding a bake sale to raise money for the end of season banquet. Team members donated 15 dozen of chocolate chips cookies, 12 dozen of oatmeal cookies, 8 dozen of sugar cookies, 10 dozen of peanut butter cookies, 6 dozen of fudge cookies, 4 dozen of lemon drop cookies, and 5 dozen of thumbprint cookies.

1. Find the fraction of the cookies that are chocolate chip cookies.

2. Find the fraction of the cookies that are peanut butter cookies.

3. Find the fraction of the cookies that are oatmeal cookies.

4. Find the fraction of the cookies that are thumbprint cookies.

5. Find the fraction of the cookies that are fudge cookies.

6. Find the fraction of the cookies that are lemon drop cookies.

7. Find the fraction of the cookies that are sugar cookies.

8. Find the fraction of cookies that are oatmeal cookies or sugar cookies.

9. Find the fraction of cookies that are not chocolate chip cookies.

10. Find the fraction of cookies that are not fudge cookies or lemon drop cookies.

11. After three days of the sale, the swim team sold $\frac{3}{4}$ of the cookies. How many cookies do they have left? Draw a diagram to show how you know that your answer is correct.

Assignment

Name _____ Date _____

Fair Share of Pizza
Equivalent Fractions

1. Divide the fraction model to determine four other fractions that are equivalent to $\frac{1}{2}$.

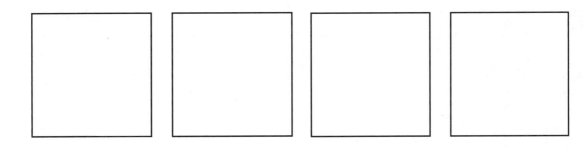

2. Divide the fraction model to determine three other fractions that are equivalent to $\frac{2}{3}$.

3. Explain what the numerator and denominator means in each of the fractions that are equivalent to $\frac{2}{3}$. Write your answer using a complete sentence.

4. Write three equivalent fractions that are equivalent to the given fraction.

$\frac{1}{5}$

$\frac{3}{7}$

$\frac{5}{8}$

Name _____ Date _____

When Twelfths Are Eighths
Simplifying Fractions

1. Your aunt made coffee cakes for dessert and cut them in different ways. Write the fraction that is represented by the fraction model. Then write the fraction in simplest form.

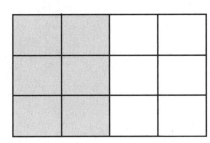

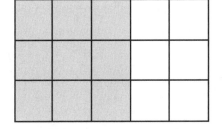

2. Draw cuts and shade in the coffee cake below to represent $\frac{16}{20}$. Then write the fraction in simplest form.

Simplest form of $\frac{16}{20}$

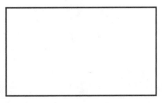

Assignment

Name _____ Date _____

When Bigger Means Smaller
Comparing and Ordering Fractions

1. Compare the fractions. Then use the symbols > or < to make each statement true.

$\frac{1}{2}$ ◯ $\frac{1}{3}$ $\frac{4}{5}$ ◯ $\frac{7}{8}$

$\frac{3}{5}$ ◯ $\frac{3}{4}$ $\frac{3}{4}$ ◯ $\frac{2}{3}$

$\frac{2}{5}$ ◯ $\frac{2}{3}$ $\frac{11}{12}$ ◯ $\frac{9}{10}$

2. Write a complete sentence to explain how you can tell which fraction is greater if both fractions have the same numerator.

3. Write a complete sentence to explain how you can tell which fraction is greater if both fractions have numerators that are one number less that their denominators.

4. Find the least common denominator (LCD) of the fractions. Then use the symbols > or < to complete the fraction statement.

$\frac{5}{8}$ ◯ $\frac{13}{20}$ LCD = _____

$\frac{19}{20}$ ◯ $\frac{54}{60}$ LCD = _____

5. Tell what method you would use to compare each pair of fractions. Then use the symbols > or < to complete the fraction statement.

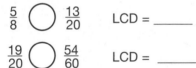

$\frac{3}{7}$ ◯ $\frac{3}{5}$

$\frac{17}{18}$ ◯ $\frac{16}{18}$

$\frac{4}{9}$ ◯ $\frac{11}{27}$

2

Name _____ Date _____

Who Gets What?
Adding and Subtracting Fractions with Like Denominators

Timothy is copying his large CD collection to MP3s so he can store them on his MP3 player.

On Monday, he copied $\frac{3}{16}$ of his music. On Tuesday, he copied $\frac{5}{16}$ of his music. On Wednesday,

he copied $\frac{7}{16}$ of his music. On Thursday, he copied the rest.

1. What fraction of his music did Timothy copy on Monday and Tuesday? Simplify your answer, if possible. Show your work.

2. What fraction of his music did Timothy copy on Tuesday and Wednesday? Simplify your answer, if possible. Show your work.

3. What fraction more of his music did Timothy copy on Wednesday than he copied on Tuesday? Simplify your answer, if possible. Show your work.

4. What fraction of his music did Timothy copy on Thursday? Remember that you can write 1 whole as $\frac{16}{16}$. Simplify your answer, if possible. Show your work.

Find each sum or difference. Simplify your answer, if possible.

5. $\frac{5}{24} + \frac{7}{24} =$

6. $\frac{7}{60} + \frac{4}{60} + \frac{9}{60} =$

7. $\frac{7}{12} - \frac{5}{12} =$

8. $\frac{15}{18} - \frac{3}{18} =$

Name _____ Date _____

Old-Fashioned Goodies
Adding and Subtracting Fractions with Unlike Denominators

1. Find the least common multiple of each pair of numbers.

   3 and 4

   4 and 6

   2 and 4

   8 and 6

2. Your little brother is making chocolate chip cookies for his class. The recipe he is using calls for $\frac{1}{4}$ cup brown sugar and $\frac{1}{2}$ cup white sugar. What is the total amount of sugar needed for this recipe? Use a complete sentence to explain how you found your answer.

3. Linn had $\frac{3}{4}$ of a cake left after her tea party. After she gave Paul $\frac{3}{8}$ of the cake, what fraction of the cake did Linn have left? Show your work.

4. Sammy read $\frac{5}{8}$ of a science fiction book. He then read another $\frac{1}{3}$ of the book. What fraction of the book did Sammy read? Show your work.

Find the sum or difference.

5. $\frac{1}{2} + \frac{3}{8} =$

6. $\frac{3}{4} - \frac{5}{8} =$

7. $\frac{1}{3} + \frac{4}{9} =$

8. $\frac{9}{10} - \frac{3}{5} =$

9. $\frac{1}{5} + \frac{2}{3} =$

10. $\frac{1}{4} + \frac{2}{3} =$

11. $\frac{5}{9} + \frac{2}{5} =$

12. $\frac{4}{5} - \frac{1}{4} =$

Name _____ Date _____

Fun and Games
Improper Fractions and Mixed Numbers

Lewis is measuring $4\frac{1}{4}$ cups of flour for a recipe. He does not want to dirty two measuring cups.

He thinks that he can use the $\frac{1}{4}$ cup measure to measure the flour.

1. Rewrite $4\frac{1}{4}$ as an improper fraction. Show all of your work.

2. How many times will Lewis have to fill the $\frac{1}{4}$ cup measure? Write your answer using a complete sentence.

Lewis wants to measure $2\frac{2}{3}$ cups of milk. He thinks that he can measure this amount using only the $\frac{1}{3}$ cup measure.

3. Rewrite $2\frac{2}{3}$ as an improper fraction. Show all of your work.

4. How many times will Lewis have to fill the $\frac{1}{3}$ cup measure? Write your answer using a complete sentence.

Rewrite each mixed number as an improper fraction. Show your work.

5. $3\frac{1}{5} =$

6. $7\frac{1}{2} =$

Rewrite each improper fraction as a mixed number. Show your work.

7. $\frac{25}{6} =$

8. $\frac{32}{9} =$

Name _____ Date _____

Parts of Parts
Multiplying Fractions

Write the multiplication problem that is shown by the area model.

1.

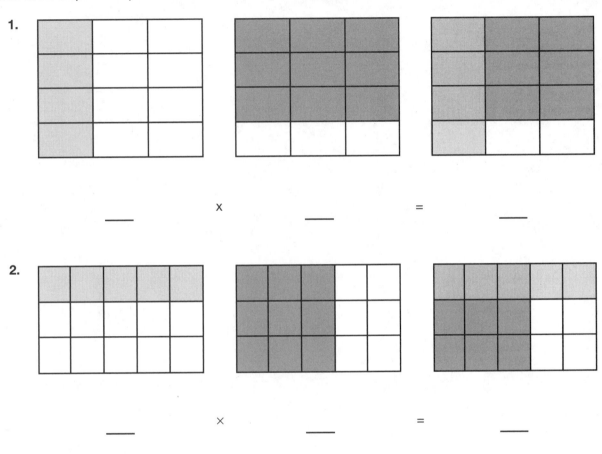

___ x ___ = ___

2.

___ x ___ = ___

Find each product. Be sure to simplify your answers, if possible.

3. $\dfrac{3}{8} \times \dfrac{1}{2} =$ $\dfrac{5}{6} \times \dfrac{3}{4} =$ $\dfrac{5}{6} \times \dfrac{3}{5} =$

$\dfrac{2}{3} \times \dfrac{3}{5} =$ $\dfrac{2}{5} \times \dfrac{10}{12} =$ $\dfrac{3}{8} \times \dfrac{4}{9} =$

4. $\dfrac{3}{4}$ of the 8th grade class tried out for the school play. If $\dfrac{5}{6}$ of those students won a part, what

part of the 8th grade will be in the play? Show your work.

Name _____ Date _____

Parts in a Part
Dividing Fractions

Jordan is going to do some baking. While gathering his ingredients, he finds that he has only $\frac{3}{4}$ cup of baking mix.

1. It takes $\frac{1}{4}$ cup of the mix to make a batch of biscuits. How many batches of biscuits can Jordan make? Show your work. Use a complete sentence to write your answer.

2. It takes $\frac{1}{2}$ cup of the mix to make a piecrust. How many piecrusts can Jordan make? Show your work. Use a complete sentence to write your answer.

3. Jordan lives $\frac{1}{2}$ mile from school. Each block in his neighborhood is $\frac{1}{10}$ mile long. How many blocks are between Jordan's house and his school? Show your work. Use a complete sentence to write your answer.

Find the quotient. Simplify your result, if possible.

5. $\frac{6}{8} \div \frac{3}{8} =$

6. $\frac{12}{12} \div \frac{3}{12} =$

7. $\frac{7}{10} \div \frac{2}{5} =$

8. $\frac{1}{6} \div \frac{2}{3} =$

9. $\frac{11}{12} \div \frac{5}{8} =$

10. $\frac{6}{15} + \frac{3}{10} =$

11. $\frac{5}{18} \div \frac{2}{12} =$

12. $\frac{3}{2} \div \frac{5}{6} =$

Assignment

Name _____ Date _____

All That Glitters
Adding and Subtracting Mixed Numbers

1. Carlos needs ribbon to wrap a present for his aunt. He has $1\frac{3}{4}$ feet of gold ribbon, $2\frac{5}{8}$ feet of blue ribbon, and $1\frac{7}{8}$ feet of red ribbon. Estimate the number of feet of ribbon Carlos needs to the nearest whole number.

2. Is your estimate in Question 1 greater than or less than the exact amount? How can you tell? Explain your reasoning using a complete sentence.

3. What is the exact amount of ribbon that Carlos used? Show your work. Write your answer using a complete sentence.

4. Carlos used only $1\frac{3}{4}$ feet of the $2\frac{5}{8}$ feet blue ribbon to wrap his aunt's present. How many feet of blue ribbon does he have left? Does he have enough blue ribbon to wrap another present if he uses the same amount of ribbon? Show your work. Write your answer using a complete sentence.

Find each sum. Show your work. Simplify your answer, if possible.

5. $9\frac{1}{4} + 3\frac{5}{6} =$

6. $3\frac{5}{6} + 4\frac{3}{10} =$

7. $1\frac{3}{8} + 2\frac{7}{12} + 3\frac{1}{4} =$

Find each difference. Simplify your answer, if possible.

8. $3\frac{7}{8} - 1\frac{3}{4} =$

9. $5\frac{1}{3} - 1\frac{5}{6} =$

10. $3\frac{1}{4} - 2\frac{5}{6} =$

11. $8 - 4\frac{3}{8} =$

3

Name _____ Date _____

Project Display
Multiplying and Dividing Mixed Numbers

1. Cynthia needs $1\frac{2}{3}$ cups of sugar for each pound of taffy. She wants to make $1\frac{1}{2}$ pounds of taffy. How many cups of sugar will she need? Show your work. Write your answer using a complete sentence.

2. Tamara is making enlargements of a picture to include in her science report. The width of the picture is $4\frac{1}{2}$ inches. She is enlarging the picture to $1\frac{3}{4}$ times its size. What will the width of the new picture be? Show your work. Write your answer using a complete sentence.

3. Farmers were able to harvest $30\frac{5}{6}$ bushels of grain from $2\frac{1}{3}$ acres. How many bushels did each acre produce? Show your work. Write your answer in a complete sentence.

Find the product or quotient. Show your work. Simplify your answer, if possible.

4. $2\frac{1}{6} \times 3\frac{4}{5} =$

5. $6\frac{1}{4} \times 3 =$

6. $3\frac{1}{4} \times 4\frac{1}{3} =$

7. $5\frac{1}{2} \times 2\frac{2}{3} =$

8. $5\frac{5}{6} \div 5 =$

9. $6\frac{3}{5} \div 1\frac{1}{2} =$

10. $9\frac{1}{5} \div 3\frac{3}{15} =$

Name _____   Date _____

Carpenter, Baker, Mechanic, and Chef
Working with Customary Units

1. Tommy was weaving different-sized squares of yarn for a class quilt. He had a skein of yarn that was $5\frac{2}{3}$ yards long. He made two squares using $2\frac{3}{8}$ feet, one square using $2\frac{1}{2}$ feet, and one

   square measuring $3\frac{2}{8}$ feet. How many feet of yarn does Tommy have left? Give your answer in

   feet and yards. Show your work. Write your answer using a complete sentence.

3

2. The baker decides that walnuts would be good in his bread. He knows that a batch for 4 loaves of bread will use $2\frac{2}{25}$ ounces of walnuts, a batch for 10 loaves of bread will use $5\frac{1}{5}$ ounces of

   walnuts, and a batch for 12 loaves of bread will use $6\frac{6}{25}$ ounces of walnuts. Will a one-pound

   bag of walnuts be enough if the baker wants to make all three batches of bread? Will he have
   enough to make another 4 loaves? Show your work. Write your answers using complete
   sentences.

Name _____ Date _____

Cents Sense
Decimals as Special Fractions

Different countries use different units of money. It is possible to use exchange rates to convert from one system of money to another. In the United Kingdom, the currency is called the pound.   Rates of exchange change from day to day.

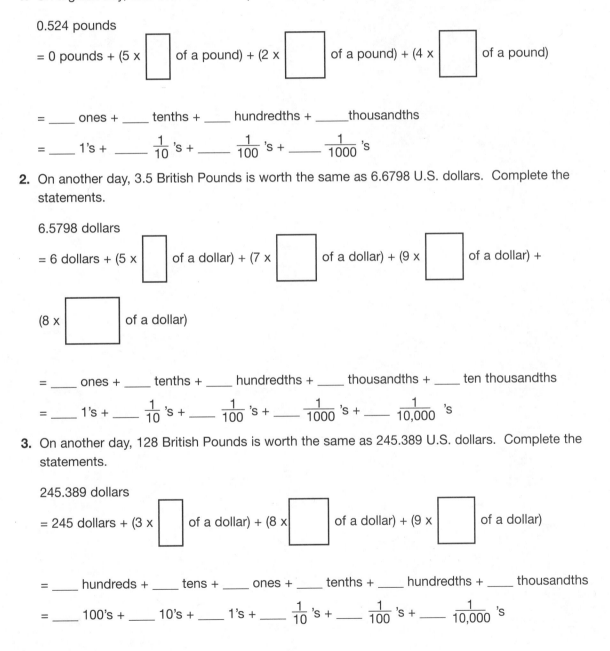

1. On a given day, one U.S. dollar is equal to 0.524 pounds.   Complete the statements.

0.524 pounds

= 0 pounds + (5 x ⬜ of a pound) + (2 x ⬜ of a pound) + (4 x ⬜ of a pound)

= ____ ones + ____ tenths + ____ hundredths + ____ thousandths

= ____ 1's + ____ $\frac{1}{10}$'s + ____ $\frac{1}{100}$'s + ____ $\frac{1}{1000}$'s

2. On another day, 3.5 British Pounds is worth the same as 6.6798 U.S. dollars. Complete the statements.

6.5798 dollars

= 6 dollars + (5 x ⬜ of a dollar) + (7 x ⬜ of a dollar) + (9 x ⬜ of a dollar) +

(8 x ⬜ of a dollar)

= ____ ones + ____ tenths + ____ hundredths + ____ thousandths + ____ ten thousandths

= ____ 1's + ____ $\frac{1}{10}$'s + ____ $\frac{1}{100}$'s + ____ $\frac{1}{1000}$'s + ____ $\frac{1}{10,000}$'s

3. On another day, 128 British Pounds is worth the same as 245.389 U.S. dollars. Complete the statements.

245.389 dollars

= 245 dollars + (3 x ⬜ of a dollar) + (8 x ⬜ of a dollar) + (9 x ⬜ of a dollar)

= ____ hundreds + ____ tens + ____ ones + ____ tenths + ____ hundredths + ____ thousandths

= ____ 100's + ____ 10's + ____ 1's + ____ $\frac{1}{10}$'s + ____ $\frac{1}{100}$'s + ____ $\frac{1}{10,000}$'s

4

Assignment

Name _____ Date _____

What's In a Place?
Place Value and Expanded Form

1. The fastest average speed recorded for a stage of the Tour de France is 50.349 kilometers per hour. Identify the place value of the given digit for this speed.

   What is the place value of the 5?

   What is the place value of the 4?

   What is the place value of the 3?

   What is the place value of the 0?

   What is the place value of the 9?

2. The winning time for the 200-meter 4-man relay in the 2004 Summer Olympics was 175.91 seconds. Identify the place value of the given digit for this time.

   What digit is in the ones place?

   What digit is in the hundredths place?

   What digit is in the hundreds place?

   What digit is in the tenths place?

   What digit is in the tens place?

3. Rewrite the word form of each decimal as a number.

   Five hundred eighty three and seven tenths

   Thirty and twenty-one hundredths

   One hundred fifty and one hundred thirty-five thousands

   Two and five thousandths

   Four hundred thirty-seven thousandths

4. Write each decimal in word form. Remember to write the decimal point as the word "and."

   31.5

   104.29

   300.03

   6.025

4

Assignment

Name _____ Date _____

My Dog Is Bigger Than Your Dog
Decimals as Fractions: Comparing and Rounding Decimals

Rewrite each decimal as a mixed number.

1. 13.242 =

2. 1.708 =

3. 3.754 =

4. 125.026 =

5. The table below lists rainfall records for Memphis, Tennessee for certain days in January according to the National Weather Service. Place the rainfall amounts in order from least to greatest.

Rank	1	2	3	4	5	6	7	8
Amount	2.58	3.33	2.13	2.86	2.92	1.83	4.53	4.40
Year	1875	1951	1949	1939	1880	1913	1930	1946

6. The table below lists the life expectancy at birth in various countries according to the CIA World Fact Book. Round each age as indicated in the table.

Country	Life Expectancy at Birth (years)	Round to the Nearest Ten	Round to the Nearest One	Round to the Nearest Tenth
Aruba	79.14			
United States	77.71			
China	72.25			
India	64.35			
Botswana	33.87			

4

Name _____ Date _____

Making Change and Changing Hours
Adding and Subtracting Decimals

1. Jenny works in a convenience store. She wants to find how much time she spends traveling to and from work. She notices that the amount of time to get to work depends on the day that she is driving. She travels 1.3 hours on Monday, 1.05 hours on Tuesday, and 0.95 hour on Wednesday.

   Draw the outlines for the base-ten pieces to represent each decimal. Then use the base-ten pieces to find the total time spent traveling for the week.

4

2. Draw the outlines for the base ten pieces to represent each decimal and the sum.

   $1.73 + 0.05 =$

   $1.1 + 0.9 + 1.03 =$

3. A customer paid Jenny for a 39 cent candy bar with a $10 bill. Jenny returned 61 cents. What mistake did Jenny make? Explain how she should correct her mistake.

Find each sum or difference. Use estimation to check your answer.

4. $2.231 + 10.6 =$ 5. $6.7 + 13.3 =$

6. $2.35 - 0.66 =$ 7. $4.7 + 0.32 =$

Assignment

Name _____ Date _____

Rules Make the World Go Round
Multiplying Decimals

A grocery store is selling ground beef for $1.89 per pound.

1. How much does it cost to buy 2.5 pounds? Round your answer to the nearest cent.

2. How much does it cost to buy 7.25 pounds? Round your answer to the nearest cent.

3. How much would it cost to buy 4.35 pounds? Round your answer to the nearest cent.

4. Spring Hill Park is on a rectangular piece of land that measures 0.75 mile by 1.25 miles. Draw and label a rectangle to represent the park. Then find the area of the park by multiplying the park's length by its width.

4

5. The table shows the running speeds in feet per second of several animals. Complete the table by finding the distance that each animal can run for the given number of seconds.

Animal	Speed (feet per second)	Time (seconds)	Distance (feet)
Quarter horse	69.7	12	
Rabbit	51.33	35.5	
Giraffe	46.93	50.5	
Chicken	13.2	100.25	

Perform the indicated multiplication.

6. $25 \times 0.31 =$

7. $890 \times 0.23 =$

8. $1 \times 0.23 =$

9. $7 \times 6.59 =$

10. $52 \times 0.86 =$

11. $7.05 \times 3.72 =$

Assignment

Name _____ Date _____

The Better Buy
Dividing Decimals

1. Use the base-ten pieces to show 0.18 ÷ 6.

Use estimation to place the decimal point in the correct position in each quotient.

2.		3.		4.		5.	

2. $3\overline{)4.2}$ quotient 14

3. $21\overline{)487.2}$ quotient 232

4. $4\overline{)93}$ quotient 2325

5. $8\overline{)204.8}$ quotient 256

Find each quotient. Estimate to check that your answer is reasonable.

6. $8\overline{)0.48}$

7. $15\overline{)16.2}$

8. $231.2 \div 17$

9. $256.186 \div 20$

10. The winning time for the middle school 4-person 100-meter relay was 62.59 seconds. Suppose that each runner ran exactly the same amount of time. What would the time be for each runner? Show your work at the right. Write your answer using a complete sentence.

Assignment

Name _____   Date _____

Bonjour!
Working with Metric Units

Which metric unit of length would be most appropriate for measuring each item? From the measurements in the box, choose a reasonable estimate of the measurement of each item.

25 centimeters	2 meters	20 meters
240 kilometers	100 meters	8 centimeters

1. Height of a doorway

2. Length of a shoe

3. Distance from Los Angeles to San Diego

4. Height of a school building

5. Width of a calculator

Which metric unit of capacity would be most appropriate for measuring the amount contained in each item? From the measurements in the box, choose a reasonable estimate of the capacity of each item.

1 milliliter	40 liters	8 kiloliters
2 liters	0.001 milliliter	40 milliliters

6. Bathtub

7. Juice box

8. Raindrop

9. Swimming pool

10. Bottle of soda

Which metric unit of mass would be most appropriate for measuring the mass of each item? From the measurements in the box, choose a reasonable estimate of the mass of each item.

1 kilogram	10,000 kilograms	2 kilograms
400 grams	2000 kilograms	2.5 grams

11. Automobile

12. Pair of shoes

13. Penny

14. Bag of sugar

15. Loaf of bread

Name _____ Date _____

Heard It and Read It
Ratios and Fractions

Write each phrase as a ratio in two ways.

1. The bakery had 5 loaves of wheat bread and 6 loaves of rye bread.

2. On the farm were 3 roosters and 25 hens.

3. Alicia spent 30 minutes reading and 80 minutes using the computer.

4. The bracelet had 13 diamonds and 20 emeralds.

5. At the football game, there were 12 cheerleaders and 25 football players.

6. Write one ratio for each row in the table. Be sure to include the quantity names. If possible, simplify the ratio.

Club Membership At City High			
	Boys	**Girls**	**Total students**
Spanish Club	32	16	48
Algebra Club	16	8	24
Drama Club	18	18	36
Music Club	15	45	60

© 2005 Carnegie Learning, Inc.

Assignment

Name _____ Date _____

Equal or Not, That Is the Question
Writing and Solving Proportions

1. Bill is painting his room a certain shade of green. The paint is a mixture of 3 parts blue paint to 2 parts yellow paint. To get the correct shade of green, how much yellow paint should he add to 6 quarts of blue paint? Find an equivalent ratio to determine the unknown quantity. Show your work.

2. LaShaya answered 9 of 10 questions correctly on her math quiz. Her twin sister LaTeisha answered 22 out of 25 questions correctly. Did they have the same ratio of correct problems to total problems? Use the product of the means and extremes to determine the answer. Show your work. The write a complete sentence to explain your answer.

5

For each proportion, find an equivalent ratio to determine the unknown quantity. Check your answer using the product of the means and extremes.

3. $\dfrac{16 \text{ miles}}{90 \text{ minutes}} = \dfrac{? \text{ miles}}{270 \text{ minutes}}$

4. $\dfrac{16 \text{ sandwiches}}{3 \text{ bags}} = \dfrac{? \text{ sandwiches}}{12 \text{ bags}}$

5. $\dfrac{72 \text{ dollars}}{12 \text{ hours}} = \dfrac{? \text{ dollars}}{6 \text{ hours}}$

6. $\dfrac{9 \text{ tons}}{3 \text{ days}} = \dfrac{12 \text{ tons}}{? \text{ days}}$

7. $\dfrac{112 \text{ ounces}}{? \text{ cans}} = \dfrac{24 \text{ ounces}}{3 \text{ cans}}$

8. $\dfrac{3 \text{ goals}}{2 \text{ games}} = \dfrac{9 \text{ goals}}{? \text{ games}}$

9. $\dfrac{? \text{ dollars}}{21 \text{ pounds}} = \dfrac{6 \text{ dollars}}{12 \text{ pounds}}$

10. $\dfrac{48 \text{ books}}{? \text{ shelves}} = \dfrac{36 \text{ books}}{3 \text{ shelves}}$

Name _____ Date _____

The Survey Says
Using Ratios and Rates

	Population	Number of FM Radio Stations	Number of AM Radio Stations
United States	295,734,134	8950	4854
France	60,656,178	3500	41
Germany	82,431,390	787	51
United Kingdom	60,441,457	431	219

1. Write a rate to describe the number of people per FM radio station in each of the four countries listed. Be sure to label the quantities.

5

2. Write each rate that you wrote in Question 1 as a unit rate. Be sure to label the quantities being compared. Round the numerator of the unit rate to the nearest whole number.

3. Order the rates that you wrote in Question 2 from least to greatest.

4. Write a rate to describe the number of people per AM radio station in each of the four countries listed. Be sure to label the quantities being compared.

5. Write each rate that you wrote in Question 4 as a unit rate. Be sure to label the quantities being compared. Round the numerator of the unit rate to the nearest whole number.

6. Order the ratios you wrote in question 5 from least to greatest.

Assignment

Name _____ Date _____

Who's Got Game?
Using Proportions to Solve Problems

Write and solve a proportion to answer each problem. Show your work.

1. Tommy types 54 words per minute, with an average of 3 mistakes. How many mistakes would you expect Tommy to make if he typed 300 words? Write your answer using a complete sentence.

2. Jackie burns 250 calories per hour doing aerobics. She has to burn 2000 calories to lose one pound. How long will Jackie have to work out to lose 5 pounds?

3. Six cans of fruit juice costs $2.50. Ned needs to buy 72 cans for a camping trip for the Outdoor Club. How much will he spend?

4. A safe following distance is two car lengths for every ten miles per hour that you are traveling. If you are traveling at 65 miles per hour, how many car lengths is a safe following distance?

Use any process to solve each proportion. Be sure to show all of your work.

5. $\dfrac{5 \text{ minutes}}{3 \text{ gallons}} = \dfrac{x \text{ minutes}}{27 \text{ gallons}}$

6. $\dfrac{500 \text{ calories}}{5 \text{ miles}} = \dfrac{50 \text{ calories}}{x \text{ miles}}$

7. $\dfrac{13 \text{ bats}}{8 \text{ hits}} = \dfrac{65 \text{ bats}}{x \text{ hits}}$

8. $\dfrac{5 \text{ grams of protein}}{3 \text{ grams of fat}} = \dfrac{x \text{ grams of protein}}{21 \text{ grams of fat}}$

Name _____ Date _____

Certain fractions, decimals, and percents are used often. The amounts in the table below are used frequently for sales, commission amounts, interest rates, and tax rates. Fill in the missing fraction, decimal, or percent to complete the table.

Fraction	Decimal	Percent
	0.01	1%
	0.1	10%
	0.125	12.5%
	0.2	20%
	0.25	25%
	0.3333	%
	0.5	50%
	0.375	37.5%
	0.6667	%
	0.75	75%
	0.8	80%
	0.9	90%

Name _____ Date _____

Brain Waves
Making Sense of Percents

1. Find each percent of 45.

   What is 1% of 45?

   What is 10% of 45?

   What is 40% of 45?

   What is 95% of 45?

   What is 225% of 45?

2. Find each percent of 250.

   What is 1% of 250?

   What is 10% of 250?

   What is 22% of 250?

   What is 85% of 250?

   What is 150% of 250?

3. Jai is a 28% shooter in basketball. That means when he shoots a free throw he makes a basket 28% of the time. Jai shoots 120 free throws in a season. How many baskets will he be likely to make? Use benchmark percents of 1% and 10% to help you find the answer. Write your answers using complete sentences.

   What is 1% of 120?

   What is 10% of 120?

   What is 20% of 120?

   What is 8% of 120?

4. In Tampa, Florida the suns shines about 66% of the year. About how many days does the sun shine in Tampa? Use benchmark percents of 1% and 10% to help you find the answer. Then use complete sentences to explain your answer.

© 2005 Carnegie Learning, Inc.

Name _____ Date _____

Commissions, Taxes, and Tips
Finding the Percent of a Number

The items below were purchased in a city with a sales tax rate of 7%. Find the amount of sales tax on each purchase.

1. A DVD for $18.00

2. A computer hard drive for $40.00

3. A bathing suit for $25.00

4. A bicycle for $150.00

An advertising salesperson receives a 15% commission on all of the sales that she makes. Calculate the commission on each sale.

5. A quarter-page ad for $250

6. A half-page ad for $450

7. A full-page ad for $800

8. The inside back cover ad for $1200

A shoe store is having a 25% off sale on all of its shoes. Calculate the discount on each of the pairs of shoes that sell for the original price listed below.

9. Men's running shoes for $85.00

10. Women's cross training shoes for $50

11. Softball cleat shoes for $29.95

12. Golf shoes for $120

Assignment

Name _____ Date _____

Find it on the Fifth Floor
Finding One Whole, or 100%

1. Jamie and his friends have summer jobs. They need to save some of their money for college expenses. They each save a percent of their summer earnings. Find the money each friend saved using the information given in the table. Solve by finding 1% of the amount saved and then multiplying that answer by the percent saved.

Name	Percent Saved	Amount Saved	Total Earnings
Jamie	20%	$124	
Sammi	25%	$152	
Keith	10%	$135	
Tara	15%	$117	

Write a proportion to answer each question. Then solve the proportion.

2. 50 is 40% of what number?

3. 8% of what number is 2?

4. 12 is 30% of what number?

5. You know that 20% of a number is 30. What is the number?

6. Tara read 45 pages of her summer novel on the bus to work. If this is 18% of the novel, how many pages are in the novel?

Name _____ Date _____

It's Your Money
Finding Percents Given Two Numbers

1. Five co-workers are trying to figure out who received the highest percent of their wages for a bonus. Each person's total wages and bonus are listed in the table. Complete the table by calculating the percent bonus. Use any method to determine the percent. Show your work.

Person	Wages	Total Bonus	Percent Bonus
Leah	$4500	$157.50	3.5%
Ratha	$23,400	$538.20	2.3%
Ed	$35,350	$636.30	1.8%
Chris	$7500	$315.00	4.2%
Mary	$14,500	$362.50	2.5%

2. The number 14 is what percent of 200?

3. The number 28 is what percent of 200?

4. What percent of 200 is 56?

5. What percent of 200 is 112?

6. What percent of 50 is 225?

Name _____ Date _____

So You Want to Buy a Car
Percent Increase and Percent Decrease

Use ratios to find the percent increase or percent decrease in each problem.

1. A dress that normally sells for $72 is on sale for $45. What is the percent decrease in the price?

2. A home purchased for $120,000 in 2002 is sold for $155,000 in 2005. What is the percent increase in the price?

3. The CD Warehouse purchases CD's for $6.00 each and sells them for $9.00. What is the percent increase in the price?

4. The CD Warehouse is having a clearance sale. A CD player that originally sells for $60 is now priced at $36. What is the percent decrease in the price?

5. The local high school sold 1914 tickets last year to its spring musical. That was 174 more ticket sold that last year. What is the percent increase in the number of tickets sold?

6. After exercising, Ken's heart rate went from 74 beats per minute to 148 beats per minute. What is the percent increase in his heart rate?

7. Bargain Basement is having a going-out-of-business sale. All merchandise is first marked down 50%. It is then marked down an additional 50%. Are they giving their merchandise away for free? Use an example and write complete sentences to explain your thinking.

Name _____ Date _____

I Love New York
Negative Numbers in the Real World

1. The highest temperature ever recorded on Earth was 136° F at Al Aziziyah, Libya in Africa. The lowest temperature ever recorded on Earth was −129°F at Vostok Station in Antarctica. Write each temperature as an integer. Use the number line to find the number of degrees between these two temperatures.

2. The highest recorded temperature in Anchorage, Alaska was 86° on June 25, 1953. The lowest recorded temperature in that city was −38° recorded on February 3, 1947. Write each temperature as an integer. Find the number of degrees between these two temperatures. Write your answer using a complete sentence.

7

3. The highest point in the U.S. is Mount McKinley, Alaska at about 6773 yards above sea level. The lowest point in the U.S. is the Badwater Basin in Death Valley, California at about 87 yards below sea level. Write both elevations as integers. Use the number line to find the number of yards between the lowest and highest points.

4. The deepest point in the ocean is the Marianas Trench in the Pacific Ocean at about 6.9 miles below sea level. The highest point in the world is Mount Everest in the Himalayan Mountains at about 5.5 miles. Write each height as an integer. Use the number line to find the approximate number of miles between the lowest and highest points.

Assignment

Name _____ Date _____

Going Up?
Adding Integers

Use the number line to illustrate each statement.

1. Write and evaluate an addition statement in which the addends are both positive.

2. Write and evaluate an addition expression in which both addends are negative.

3. Write and evaluate an addition expression in which the addends have different signs.

4. Write an addition expression in which the sum is zero.

Find each sum without using a number line.

5. $4 + (-8) =$

6. $15 + (-7) =$

7. $-13 + 18 =$

8. $-25 + 17 =$

9. $-5 + 5 =$

10. $9 + (-9) =$

11. $-5 + (-6) =$

12. $-33 + (-7) =$

Name _____ Date _____

Test Scores, Grades, and More
Subtracting Integers

Use the number line to find the difference. Show your work.

1. $12 - 5 =$

2. $7 - (-6) =$

3. $-4 - (-8) =$

4. $-10 - (-4) =$

5. $-5 - 10 =$

Find each sum without using a number line.

6. $7 - (-13) =$

7. $10 - (-1) =$

8. $-16 - 3 =$

9. $-9 - 7 =$

10. $-1 - (-2) =$

11. $-5 - (-5) =$

12. $19 - (-19) =$

13. $-8 - (-8) =$

14. $40 - (-20) =$

15. $-800 - (-300) =$

Assignment

Name _____ Date _____

Checks and Balances
Multiplying and Dividing Integers

Represent each problem as multiplication problem. Then use repeated addition to solve the problem.

1. Tesha withdrew $30 each week from her savings account to pay for her dance lesson. How much money did she withdraw in four weeks?

2. The average temperature dropped 2 degrees per hour for 5 hours. How many degrees did the temperature drop during that time period?

Rewrite each multiplication problem as the product of –1 and a positive integer.

3. $-3 \times -4 =$

4. $-8 \times -7 =$

5. $-4 \times -6 \times 5 =$

Rewrite each division problem as a related multiplication problem. Then find the quotient.

6. $-25 \div 5$

7. $-49 \div (-7)$

Find each product or quotient.

8. $3 \times 4 =$

   $3 \times (-4) =$

   $-3 \times (-4) =$

9. $12 \div 3 =$

   $-12 \div 3 =$

   $12 \div (-3) =$

10. $2 \times 5 =$

    $2 \times (-5) =$

    $-2 \times (-5) =$

11. $10 \div 5 =$

    $-10 \div 5 =$

    $-10 \div (-5) =$

12. $6 \times 7 =$

    $-6 \times 7 =$

    $-6 \times (-7) =$

13. $42 \div 6 =$

    $-42 \div 6 =$

    $-42 \div (-6) =$

Name _____ Date _____

Weight of a Penny
Additive and Multiplicative Inverses and Absolute Value

1. The table shows the lowest record temperatures for several states. Write the absolute value of the number that represents each temperature in the table. The first one is done for you.

State	Temperature (degrees Fahrenheit)	Absolute Value of Temperature
Florida	–2	
Tennessee	–32	
Texas	–23	
Hawaii	2	
Idaho	–60	

Find the sum or difference inside the absolute value symbol. Then find the absolute value of the result.

2. $\left| -6 + 5 \right| = \left| \boxed{} \right| =$

3. $\left| -11 + 15 \right| = \left| \boxed{} \right| =$

4. $\left| 8 + (-9) \right| = \left| \boxed{} \right| =$

5. $\left| 22 + (-7) \right| = \left| \boxed{} \right| =$

6. $\left| -7 + (-3) \right| = \left| \boxed{} \right| =$

7. $\left| -10 + (-10) \right| = \left| \boxed{} \right| =$

Find the distance between the numbers

8. Distance between –2 and 3 = $\left| \boxed{} \right| =$

9. Distance between 12 and –12 = $\left| \boxed{} \right| =$

10. Graph each number on the number line. Then graph the opposite of the number.

    –12   7

11. A fellow student says that $\left| -7 + 4 \right|$ is the same as $\left| -7 \right| + \left| 4 \right|$. Is she correct? Use a complete sentence to explain why or why not.

Assignment

Name _____ Date _____

Exploring the Moon
Powers of Ten

1. The world population in 1650 was approximately 550,000,000. By 1979, the world population had grown to about 4,336,000,000. Write each population. Write each number in expanded form using powers of ten.

2. Write each population in expanded form using powers of 10.

   Asia: 27,730,000,000 =
   Europe: 4,820,000,000 =
   Africa: 4,660,000,000 =

3. A common influenza virus measures 0.0001 millimeters across. Write this measurement in expanded form using powers of ten. (Use negative powers of 10 to represent numbers less than 1.)

4. For each situation, write the measure of energy generated in standard form. (A joule is a unit of energy.)

   Hurricane: 4×10^{15} joules
   Atom bomb: $8 \times 10^{13} + 4 \times 10^{12}$ joules
   Man running: $2 \times 10^{6} + 5 \times 10^{5}$ joules
   Woman running: $1 \times 10^{6} + 8 \times 10^{5}$ joules
   Chirp of a cricket: 9×10^{-4} joules
   Moonlight on a face: 8×10^{-5} joules

Use the rules below to find each product or quotient.

When you multiply by powers of 10 that are greater than 1, you move the decimal point one place to the right for each zero in the power of 10.
When you multiply by powers of 10 that are less than 1, you move the decimal point one place to the left for each decimal place in the power of 10.
When you divide by powers of 10 that are greater than 1, you move the decimal point one place to the left for each zero in the power of 10.
When you divide by powers of 10 that are less than 1, you move the decimal point one place to the right for each decimal place in the power of 10.

6. $124 \times 10 =$

7. $1045 \times 0.1 =$

8. $981 \times 0.01 =$

9. $3.217 \times 1000 =$

10. $549 \div 100 =$

11. $3.945 \div 10 =$

12. $2.137 \div 0.1 =$

13. $24,903 \div 0.001 =$

Assignment

Name _____ Date _____

Expanding Our Perspective
Scientific Notation

In the table are some facts about the universe. The very large numbers are written as a numeral or using scientific notation. Complete the table.

Description	Numeral	Scientific Notation
Distance from earth to the sun	93,000,000 mi	
Temperature of the sun at the core	27,000,000°F	
Number of protons in a gram		6.022×10^{23}
Mass of a proton	0.00000000000000000000000016726 kg	
Mass of an electron		9.11×10^{-28}g
Mass of Earth		5.974×10^{24} kg
Mass of the sun		1.9889×10^{30} kg
Mass of a virus	0.00000000000000000035 g	
Wavelength of violet light	0.0000004 m	
Wavelength of gamma rays	0.00000000000001 m	
Distance light travels in a year		9.46×10^{15} m
Approximate value of the U.S. debt	$7,787,000,000,000	
Diameter of an atom		4.2×10^{-8} m
Diameter of an electron		5.64×10^{-15} m
Width of the Milky Way Galaxy	851,400,000,000,000,000,000 m	

Name _____ Date _____

Life in a Small Town
Picture Algebra

The owner of the coffee shop in the town that you are studying keeps track of her sales of food and beverages. On one particular day, the store had a total of $168 in sales. The food sales were $28 more than the beverage sales. How much were the food and beverage sales that day?

1. In the space below, draw a picture to represent the situation. Label the unknown parts with a variable and the known parts with their values. Do not worry about making the drawing to scale.

2. Use the picture to find out how much the coffee shop sold in food and how much in beverages.

Food sales:
Beverage sales:

3. Write a word equation to represent the drawing in Question 1.

High school students in the town that you are studying go to a school with students from two other towns. The total number of students in the high school is 429. Your town, Town A, has 2 more than twice as many students as Town B. Town C has 23 more students than your town.

4. In the space below, draw a picture to represent the situation. Label the unknown parts with a variable and the known parts with their values. Do not worry about making the drawing to scale.

5. Use the picture to find out how many students are from each town.

Students in Town A:

Students in Town B:

Students in Town C:

6. Write a word equation to represent the drawing in Question 4.

8

Name _____   Date _____

Computer Games, CDs, and DVDs
Writing, Evaluating, and Simplifying Expressions

The coffee shop has a special promotion in which you can buy a card for $5.00 and purchase large coffee drinks for a month for only $1.50 each.

1. Use this information to complete the table below.

Month	Number of Drinks Purchased	Cost of Discount Card	Total Cost of drinks (with card purchased)
January	15	$5.00	
February	20		
March	10		
April			$17.00
May			$14.00
June	4		

2. In the table, what values change?

3. In the table, what values do not change?

4. Do the values in one column of the table depend on the values in another column? Use a complete sentence to explain.

5. Use a complete sentence to explain how you found the total cost of drinks for each month.

6. Complete the table below.

m	$4m + 8$
	20
6	
−2	
	8
0.5	

Name _____ Date _____

Selling Cars
Solving One-Step Equations

The Media Store runs a promotion in July to increase summer business. They take $2 off of every DVD in the store. Complete the table below.

Movie	Regular Price	Sale Price
Speed XXIV	$17	$15
The Furious and the Fast	$12	$10
Planet Wars	$21	$19
Saturday the Fourteenth XIII	$6	$4

1. How did you find the sale price, given the regular price? Use a complete sentence to explain your answer.

2. Write an expression to represent the sale price, given the regular price.

Use any method to solve each equation.

3. $x + 33 = 97$

4. $7 + x = 24$

5. $m - 325 = 399$

6. $m - 3.5 = 22.6$

7. $5y = 17$

9. $12.5y = 225$

9. $\dfrac{w}{22} = 15$

10. $\dfrac{w}{4} = 120.3$

Assignment

Name _____ Date _____

A Park Ranger's Work is Never Done
Solving Two-Step Equations

A local park rents cabins for people who want to vacation by the forest. The fee for the rental is $27 per night. There is also a $55 cleaning and maintenance charge that is added to the total bill.

1. What would the total cost be for a 3-day weekend rental? Write your answer using a complete sentence.

2. What would the total cost be for a 7-day week-long rental? Write your answer using a complete sentence.

3. Define a variable for the number of days that a cabin is rented. Use the variable to write an expression that represents the cost to rent the cabin, given the number of days that the cabin is rented.

4. How many days could the cabin have been rented if the total rental fee is $190? Show your work. Write your answer using a complete sentence.

5. Write an equation that you can use to find the number of days that you could rent the cabin for $28. Solve the equation. Does you answer make sense? Write your answer using a complete sentence.

Solve each two-step equation. Show your work.

6. $12z + 8 = 44$

7. $123.4 = 5t - 8.8$

Name _____ Date _____

Where's the Point?
Plotting Points in the Coordinate Plane

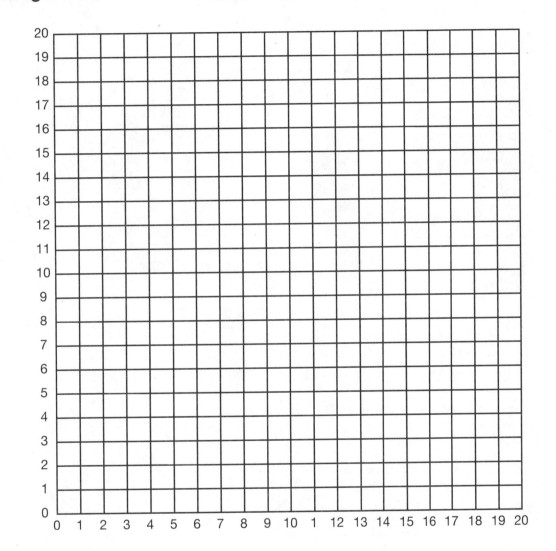

Plot and label each point in the coordinate plane.

1. A (5, 3)

2. B (0, 4)

3. C (12, 0)

4. D (13, 3)

5. E (3, 17)

6. F (20, 2)

7. G (1, 12)

8. H (16, 14)

9. J (1, 6)

10. K (5, 19)

Assignment

Name _____ Date _____

Get Growing!
Using Tables and Graphs

Lewis is researching a type of fish called carp. He discovers that one variety of carp can grow 5 pounds during each year of its life. He decided to purchase a very young carp of this variety that weighed 2 pounds.

1. How much will his carp weigh after 1 year? Write your answer using a complete sentence.

2. Define a variable for the amount of time in years that Lewis has had the carp. Write an expression that represents the weight of the carp in terms of the number of years Lewis has had it.

3. Use the expression that you wrote in Question 2 to complete the table.

Time (years)	Weight (pounds)
0	
1.5	
	12
	17
5	
6.5	
	37
	42

Solve the equations below using any method.

4. 6n + 17 = 53

5. 245 = 25n − 5

6. $\dfrac{x}{3} + 2 = 14$

7. $\dfrac{w}{4} - 7 = -5$

8

Name _____ Date _____

Saving Energy
Solving Problems Using Multiple Representations

Sandy is driving east from San Francisco along Route 80. The graph below represents the relationship between the time that Sandy has driven and the distance that she has driven.

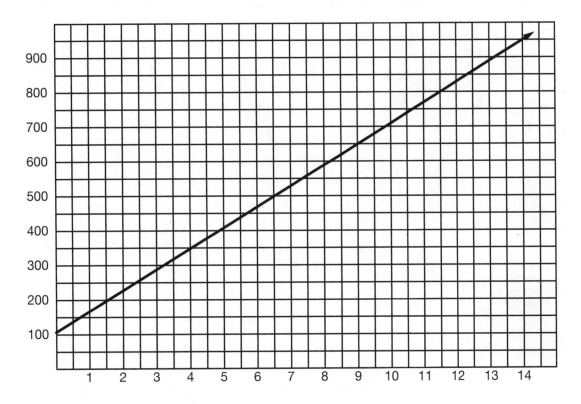

1. How far will Sandy be from San Francisco in 5 hours?

2. How far will Sandy be from San Francisco in 10 hours?

3. How far will Sandy be from San Francisco in 1 hour?

4. How fast is Sandy driving?

5. Write an equation to find the number of hours that Sandy drove if she drove for 340 miles.

Assignment

Name _____ Date _____

Figuring All of the Angles
Angles and Angle Pairs

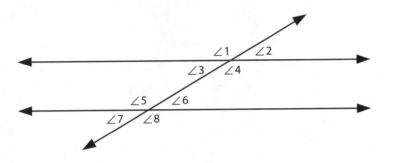

In the figure of a gate above, the measure of ∠1 is 135°. Complete each statement.

1. The measure of ∠ 2 is _____ .

2. ∠ 1 and ∠ 2 are _____ angles.

3. The measure of ∠ 3 is _____ .

4. ∠ 1 and ∠ 3 are _____ angles.

5. The measure of ∠4 is _____ .

6. ∠ 1 and ∠ 4 are _____ angles.

7. The measure of ∠5 is _____ .

8. ∠ ____ and ∠5 are vertical angles.

9. The measure of 6 is _____ .

10. ∠ ____ and ∠6 are corresponding angles.

11. The measure of ∠7 is _____ .

12. ∠ ____ and ∠7 are supplementary angles.

13. ∠ ____ and ∠7 are supplementary angles.

14. Write all of the relationships that you can think of that exists between the angles in the figure at the right.

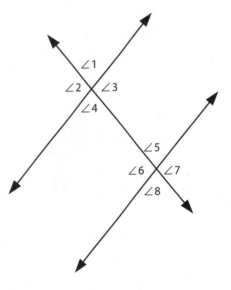

Assignment

Name _____ Date _____

Collection of Triangles
Classifying Triangles

1. Use a ruler to draw an isosceles triangle that has a right angle.

2. Use a ruler to draw an isosceles triangle that has an obtuse angle.

3. Use a ruler to draw an isosceles triangle that has 3 acute angles.

The side lengths of a triangle are given. Classify each triangle by its side lengths.

4. 2 inches, 2 inches, 2 inches

5. 5 meters, 2 meters, 4 meters

6. 7 feet, 5 feet, 5 feet

The angle measures of a triangle are given. Classify each triangle by its angle measures.

7. 30°, 90°, 60°

8. 40°, 110°, 30°

9. 45°, 60°, 75°

10. 60°, 60°, 60°

11. In the figure at the right, the length of *AB* is equal to the length of *AE*. Use dashes to mark all sides with equal lengths. Name and classify all of the triangles in the in the figure at the right. Use a complete sentence to write your answer.

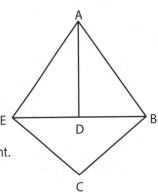

Assignment

Name _____ Date _____

The Signs Are Everywhere
Quadrilaterals and Other Polygons

1. Write all of the names for each figure.

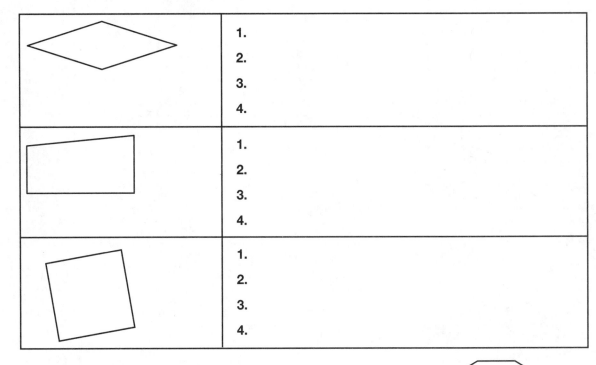

	1.
	2.
	3.
	4.
	1.
	2.
	3.
	4.
	1.
	2.
	3.
	4.

The figure at the right is 12-sided polygon called a regular dodecagon.

2. How many diagonals does a dodecagon have?

3. Into how many triangles would these diagonals divide the dodecagon?

4. What is the sum of the measures of the angles of the dodecagon?

5. What is the measure of each angle of the regular dodecagon?

6. Find the measure of the missing angles of parallelogram *CAKE*.

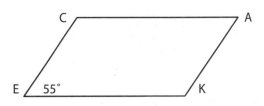

Name _____ Date _____

How Does Your Garden Grow?
Similar Polygons

For each garden plot, draw a garden plot that is similar to the given plot but larger. Then draw a garden plot that is similar to the given plot but smaller.

1.

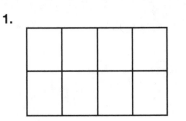

2.

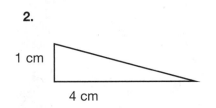

3. Decide whether the triangles are similar. If they are, then find the scale factor. Write your answer using a complete sentence.

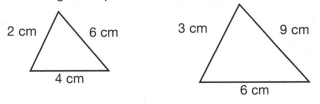

4. The rectangular gardens are similar. First find the scale factor. Then find the missing length.

Name _____ Date _____

Shadows and Mirrors
Indirect Measurement

Outside of the Boy Scouts of America building there are many flags that represent different groups within the organization. A group of scouts decided to use the shadow method to find the heights of different flagpoles.

1. The scouts find that the shorter flagpole cast a shadow that is 8 meters long. The taller flagpole casts a shadow that is 12 meters long. Find the height of the taller flagpole. Write your answer using a complete sentence.

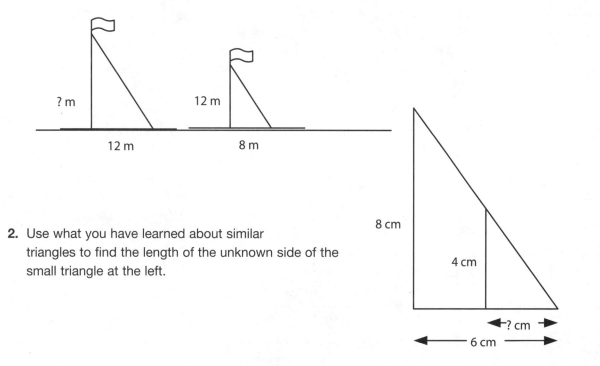

2. Use what you have learned about similar triangles to find the length of the unknown side of the small triangle at the left.

3. A tree cast a shadow 24 feet long. Casey is 5 feet tall and she cast a shadow that is 3 feet long. About how tall is the tree? Show your work. Then write your answer using a complete sentence.

Name _____ Date _____

A Geometry Game
Congruent Polygons

You want to investigate some shapes like the ones you worked with when you played the Geometry Game. Use the grid below to make new shapes that are similar to rectangle *ABCD* with the scale factors given in the table. Then complete the table.

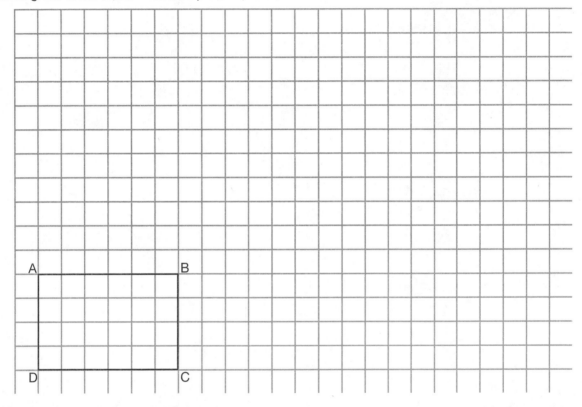

Scale factor	Perimeter of original shape	Perimeter of new shape	How many times bigger is the perimeter of the new shape?	Area of original shape	Area of new shape	How many times bigger is the area of the new shape?
1						
2						
0.5						

Now, make another rectangle that has the same area as the area of rectangle *ABCD*. Is the new rectangle congruent to rectangle *ABCD*? Is your new rectangle similar to rectangle *ABCD*?

Assignment

Name _____   Date _____

All Skate!
Perimeter and Area

1. You get a job with the maintenance department of an apartment rental company. Your boss wants you to estimate the amount of paint needed for the next month. He tells you that you can paint 400 square feet with each gallon of wall paint. Fill in the missing values to complete the table.

Job Number	Wall Width (feet)	Wall Height (feet)	Area (square feet)
1	7 feet	8 feet	
2	16 feet	8 feet	
3	12 feet	10 feet	
4	14 feet	10 feet	
5	18 feet		180 square feet
6	10 feet		120 square feet
7	16 feet		192 square feet
8		12 feet	216 square feet
9		12 feet	288 square feet

2. Find the total area to be painted for all of the jobs.

3. Use the result of Question 2 to determine the number of gallons of paint that you need to purchase to do all of the painting. Use a complete sentence to explain your reasoning.

4. Suppose that you need to put trim around the edges of the wall that has a width of 16 feet and a height of 12 feet. How many 8-foot pieces of trim do you need to purchase? Use a complete sentence to explain your reasoning.

10

Assignment

Name _____ Date _____

Round Food Around the World
Circumference and Area of a Circle

Northern Tier Gardens has hired you for a summer job installing water gardens. They have circular water garden pools available in a variety of sizes. It is important to know the area of the garden to help determine how many plants and fish the garden can support. It is also important to know the circumference because there is a metal rim around each water garden pool to provide support and to help keep dirt out.

1. The manager has asked you to create a table showing the dimensions of the company's various water gardens. He reminds you that the area of a circle can be found using the formula $A = \pi r^2$ and the circumference can be found using the formula $C = 2\pi r$. Use 3.14 for π and round each answer to the nearest hundredth.

Garden Name	Radius (feet)	Diameter (feet)	Area (square feet)	Circumference (feet)
Atlantic	2.5 feet	5 feet		
Pacifica	6 feet	12 feet		
Mediterranean	1.75 feet	3.5 feet		
Baltica	1 feet	2 feet		
Japanesque	2.25 feet	4.5 feet		
Floridian	3.25 feet	6.5 feet		

2. The garden company also makes rectangular garden pools. The table below has dimensions of some of the rectangular pools. Complete the table.

Garden Name	Length (feet)	Width (feet)	Area (square feet)	Perimeter (feet)
New Yorker	2.5 feet	5.5 feet		
Pennsylvanian	3 feet	8 feet		
Californian	4 feet	6 feet		
Arizonian	2 feet	3 feet		

10

Assignment

Name _____ Date _____

City Planning
Areas of Parallelograms, Triangles, Trapezoids, and Composite Figures

1. Give the dimensions of a rectangle that has the same area as the parallelogram pictured below. What is the area?

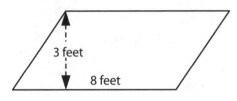

3 feet

8 feet

2. The city wants to create a garden according to the plan below. Find the area and perimeter of the garden. Write your answer using a complete sentence.

10

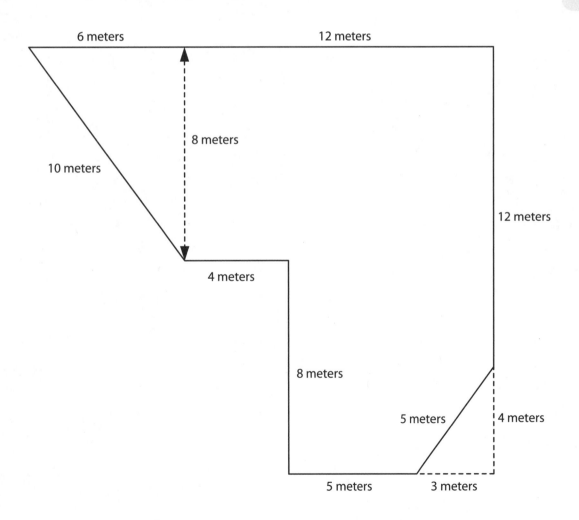

6 meters

12 meters

8 meters

10 meters

12 meters

4 meters

8 meters

5 meters

4 meters

5 meters

3 meters

Assignment

© 2005 Carnegie Learning, Inc.

Name _____ Date _____

Sports Fair and Square
Squares and Square Roots

Tech-Right Industries makes windows in various shapes, including square.

1. A customer wants a square window with an area of 49 square feet. What is the perimeter of the window? Show your work. Then write a complete sentence to explain your reasoning.

2. A customer wants a square window with a perimeter of 20 feet. What is the area of the window? Show your work. Then write a complete sentence to explain your reasoning.

10

3. A customer wants a square window with an area of 16 square feet. What is the perimeter of the window? Show your work. Then write a complete sentence to explain your reasoning.

4. A customer wants a square window with a perimeter of 14 feet. What is the area of the window? Show your work. Then write a complete sentence to explain your reasoning.

Estimate each square root to the nearest tenth.

5. $\sqrt{10} \approx$ 6. $\sqrt{30} \approx$

7. $\sqrt{75} \approx$ 8. $\sqrt{50} \approx$

9. $\sqrt{20} \approx$ 10. $\sqrt{200} \approx$

Name _____ Date _____

Are You Sure It's Square?
The Pythagorean Theorem

A fence company makes gates of different sizes. Each gate needs to have a brace installed as shown in the figure below. Use the dimensions given in the table to find the length of the brace needed for each gate. Use the Pythagorean Theorem to find the lengths. Round each length to the nearest hundredth of a foot. Show your work in the space below the table.

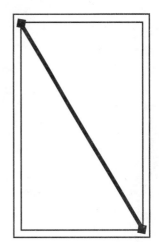

Gate Sizes and Brace Lengths		
Height (feet)	Width (feet)	Brace Length (feet)
3 feet	3 feet	
3 feet	10 feet	
4 feet	3 feet	
4 feet	10 feet	
6 feet	3 feet	
6 feet	10 feet	

Brace for 3 foot by 3 foot gate:

Brace for 3 foot by 10 foot gate:

Brace for 4 foot by 3 foot gate:

Brace for 4 foot by 10 foot gate:

Brace for 6 foot by 3 foot gate:

Brace for 6 foot by 10 foot gate:

Name _____ Date _____

A Week at Summer Camp
Using the Pythagorean Theorem

1. The field in front of the dining hall at camp is a rectangle that is 125 yards wide and 375 yards long. How far is it from one corner of the field to the opposite corner? Round your answer to the nearest whole number. Write your answer using a complete sentence.

2. You are making a picture frame in the craft cabin. The frame measures 9 inches by 12 inches. You measure the diagonal and it is 17 inches. Is the frame rectangular? Show your work and write your answer in a complete sentence.

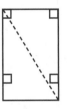

3. On the third day at camp, you go canoeing on the camp lake. You paddle from the dock due north for 500 yards and then due west for 475 yards. How far are you from the dock? Round your answer to the nearest whole number. Write your answer in a complete sentence.

10

4. You are helping to build a new door for the cabin. You measure the doorway and find that it is 3 feet wide and 7 feet tall. You measure the diagonal and find that it is 7 feet, $7\frac{1}{2}$ inches long. Is the door frame rectangular? Write your answer using a complete sentence.

5. Complete the table of Pythagorean triples below. What pattern do you see?

Leg 1	Leg 2	Hypotenuse
3 feet	4 feet	
6 feet	8 feet	
9 feet	12 feet	
12 feet	16 feet	
15 feet	20 feet	

Assignment

Name _____ Date _____

Sometimes You're Just Rained Out
Finding Simple Probabilities

You are planning an outdoor reunion in Pittsburgh. In a given year in Pittsburgh there are an average of 60 clear days, 100 partly cloudy days, and 205 cloudy days.

1. Find the probability that it will be cloudy on a randomly-chosen day.

2. Find the probability that it will be clear on a randomly-chosen day.

3. Are the probabilities that you found in Questions 1 and 2 theoretical or experimental probabilities? Use a complete sentence to explain.

4. While playing basketball, Keira made 4 out 10 of her last foul shots Tara made 10 out of 25 of her last foul shots. Who has the better probability of making the next foul shot? Use a complete sentence to explain your answer.

11

Since 1903, the National League has played the American League in the World Series. The World Series is usually won by the team winning the best out of 7 games. The series has been won in the following number of games during its first 100 years.

Number of Games	Number of Times Won with Number of Games
4 games	17 times
5 games	24 times
6 games	21 times
7 games	33 times
8 games	5 times

5. What is the probability that the next World Series will take 7 games to determine a winner?

6. What is the probability that it will take 4 games?

7. Is this theoretical or experimental probability? Use a complete sentence to explain.

Name _____ Date _____

Socks and Marbles
Finding Probabilities of Compound Events

You place the pieces M-A-T-H-E-M-A-T-I-C-S of a popular board game into a bag. You put your hand into the bag and choose a piece.

1. What is the probability that you choose a vowel?

2. What is the probability that you first choose a vowel and then you pull out another vowel without replacing the first vowel? Show your work.

You have some different bills in you pocket: one $20 bill, three $10 bills, two $5 bills, and one $1 bill.

3. What is the probability that if you reach into your pocket without looking, you will pull out a $10 bill?

4. What is the probability that after you pull out the $10 bill, you do not replace it but reach in and pull out another $10 bill? Show your work.

5. What is the probability that after you pull out the first $10 bill, you put it back and then pull out another $10 bill? Show your work.

A chess set contains the following pieces: 8 black pawns, 8 white pawns, 2 black rooks, 2 white rooks, 2 black knights, 2 white knights, 2 black bishops, 2 white bishops, 1 black queen, 1 white queen, 1 black king, and 1 white king. Find the probabilities of reaching into a bag containing the pieces and pulling out the given piece.

6. A white piece

7. A knight

8. A black knight

9. A black pawn

10. A white pawn and then without replacement a second white pawn

11. Is the event in Question 10 an independent event or dependent event?

11

© 2005 Carnegie Learning, Inc.

Assignment

Name _____ Date _____

What Do You Want to Be?
Mean, Median, Mode, and Range

You are thinking about becoming a teacher, but you are considering working in another country for a few years. You did some research and found the average beginning teacher salaries in other countries.

Country	Description	Country	Description
Switzerland	$33,209	France	$19,761
Germany	$29,697	Greece	$19,327
Denmark	$28,140	Italy	$19,188
Netherlands	$25,896	Portugal	$18,751
United States	$25,707	Sweden	$18,581
Australia	$25,661	Finland	$18,110
Spain	$24,464	New Zealand	$16,678
Norway	$22,194	Mexico	$10,465
Ireland	$21,940	Turkey	$9,116
Austria	$21,804	Czech Republic	$6,806
Iceland	$19,939	Hungary	$5,763
Total			$441,197

1. Find the mean salary for beginning teachers in these countries. Round your answer to the nearest whole dollar.

2. What is the median salary for these countries?

3. Find the mode of the data set if it exists. If it does not exist, use a complete sentence to explain why.

4. What is the range of salaries?

5. What does the mean tell you about the salaries for these different countries? Write your answer using a complete sentence.

6. What does the median tell you about the salaries for these different countries? Write your answer using a complete sentence.

7. What does the mode tell you about the salaries for these different countries? Write your answer using a complete sentence.

Name _____ Date _____

Get the Message?
Histograms

You use your cellular phone for almost all of your calls, but you noticed that your parents and older relatives do not. You surveyed the members of your family and your class and had them keep track of the number of calls that they make each day on their cellular phones. The average numbers of calls per day for each person is listed below.

21	22	10	8	2
15	13	9	14	7
7	12	9	3	8
7	15	12	5	13

1. Complete the frequency table below for this data using the intervals you chose. Use only as many columns as you need. To complete the table, use tally marks to list each occurrence in an interval. Then total the tally marks and write the frequency for each interval.

Data Intervals	1-5	6–10	11–15	16–21	21–25		
Tally							
Frequency							

2. Use the frequency table to construct a histogram below.

First, draw and label the horizontal and vertical axes.

Next, place the intervals on the horizontal scale.

Next, label the vertical scale, beginning with zero and ending with a number large enough to include all of the frequencies in the table.

Next, draw a bar to represent the frequency of each interval.

Finally, add a title to the histogram.

Name _____   Date _____

Go for the Gold!
Stem-and-Leaf Plots

You thought it might be interesting to examine the number of gold medals won by the top 20 countries at the Athens 2004 summer Olympics. You make a list of the numbers of gold medals these teams won.

4, 8, 9, 9, 10, 11, 35, 14, 3, 5, 8, 17, 27, 6, 9, 16, 4, 9, 32, 4

1. Construct a stem-and-leaf plot of the data. Include a key with your plot. Be sure to give your plot a title.

2. Find the mean of the data. Draw a square around the median of the data. Place a triangle around the mode of the data, if one exists. Find the range of the data.

3. Does displaying the data in this way help you "see" any trends? Use a complete sentence to explain any trends that you see.

You decided to compare the number of gold medals won by countries in 2004 to the number of gold medals won by countries in the 1980 summer Olympics.

2, 8, 6, 5, 7, 2, 80, 1, 2, 47,
8, 8, 3, 3, 2, 6, 2, 2, 3, 1

4. Construct a stem-and-leaf plot of the data. Then compare it to the 2004 stem-and-leaf plot. Use a complete sentence to write a statement comparing the plots.

Assignment

Name _____ Date _____

All About Roller Coasters
Box-and-Whisker Plots

Lin and Will decided that before they went to college, they wanted to ride as many roller coasters as possible. They both like coasters with a lot of drop! The length of the greatest drops on the top ten steel and top 10 wooden roller coasters are listed below.

All measurements are in feet.

Wooden
214, 155, 150.147, 141, 140, 139, 137, 129, 124

Steel
418, 400, 328, 300, 255, 229, 228, 225, 221, 219

1. What is the median drop of the wooden roller coasters in the data set?

2. What is the median drop of the steel roller coasters in the data set?

3. What is the greatest drop for each set? Wooden: _____ Steel: _____

4. What is the upper quartile for each set? Wooden: _____ Steel: _____

5. What is the least drop of each data set? Wooden: _____ Steel: _____

6. What is the lower quartile of each data set? Wooden: _____ Steel: _____

Locate the five points that you found in Questions 1–6 for each type of roller coaster on the number lines below. Then construct a box-and-whisker plot for each type of roller coaster.

Greatest Drops of Wooden Roller Coasters

Greatest Drops of Steel Roller Coasters

Assignment

Name _____ Date _____

What's Your Favorite Flavor?
Circle Graphs

The Food Service manager at the Eddy Middle School plans to add one more flavor of ice cream to the school lunch menu. The table below shows the results of a survey given to the students who were asked to choose which ice cream that they wanted to be added to the menu.

	Cookie Dough	Peach	Mint	Strawberry
Number of Votes	175	90	150	85
Fraction of Total Votes				
Fraction of Total Votes as a Decimal				
Percent of Total				

Use the percents from your table to construct a circle graph. Remember that there are 360 degrees in a circle. For each flavor, write and solve a proportion to find the number of degrees in each section of the circle graph that will represent each flavor. Include a key to the graph or label each section with the type of ice cream. Give your graph a title.

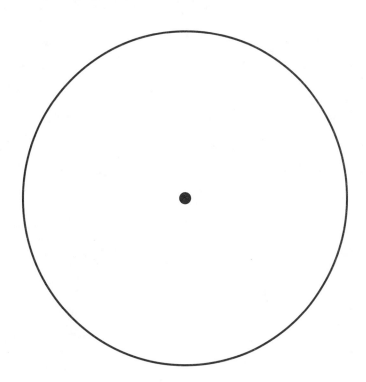

Name _____ Date _____

Expanding Our Perspective
Scientific Notation

Identify the following shapes as prism, pyramid, cylinder, cone, or sphere.

1. skyscraper

2. package

3. sea shell

4. soda can

5. The moon

6. door stop

7. top of a funnel

8. tanker on a tanker truck

9. steeple

10. grapefruit

12

Name _____ Date _____

Carnegie Candy Company
Volumes and Surface Areas of Prisms

Decide whether each is more closely related to volume or surface area.

1. The amount of air in a room

2. The amount of metal in a hamster cage

3. The amount of cardboard in a box

4. The amount of cereal that fits in a box

5. Give an example in which you would need to find volume and an example in which you would need to find surface area. Write your answers using complete sentences.

6. Find the volume and surface area of the prism.

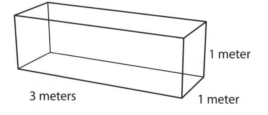

3 meters

1 meter

1 meter

7. Find the volume and surface area of the prism.

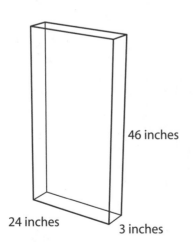

46 inches

24 inches

3 inches

12

Name _____ Date _____

The Playground Olympics
Volumes and Surface Areas of Cylinders

1. The playground has a cylindrical fountain that has a radius of 6.5 feet and a depth of 2.5 feet. What is the volume of water that will fit in the fountain? Use 3.14 for π and round your answer to two decimal places.

2. The workers at the playground use a hose that is 2 inches in diameter and 50 feet long to fill the fountain. What is the volume of water in cubic feet that will fill the hose? (Hint: 1 inch is one-twelfth of a foot.) Use 3.14 for π and round your answer to two decimal places.

3. The park has a concrete patio that is in the shape of a circle. It is 50 feet in diameter and 0.5 foot thick. What is the volume of the concrete in the patio? Use 3.14 for π and round your answer to two decimal places.

12

4. The Alaska Pipeline, finished in 1977, was created to move oil from the North Slope Oil Fields to the ice free port of Valdez, Alaska. It is 800 miles long and 4 feet in diameter. What is the volume of oil in cubic feet contained in the pipeline? (Hint: 5280 feet is 1 mile.) Use 3.14 for π.

5. How much steel was needed to make the Alaska Pipeline? Use 3.14 for π and round your answer to two decimal places.

6. The dimensions of a mailing tube are 3 inches in diameter and 36 inches long. What is the area of cardboard needed to make the mailing tube? Use 3.14 for π and round your answer to two decimal places.

7. What is the volume of space in the mailing tube? Use 3.14 for π and round your answer to two decimal places.

8. A farm silo in the shape of a cylinder measures 3 meters in diameter by 12 meters high. How much feed will the silo hold? Use 3.14 for π and round your answer to two decimal places.

Assignment

Name _____ Date _____

The Rainforest Pyramid
Volumes and Surface Areas of Pyramids and Cones

1. The Rainforest Pyramid in Galveston, Texas, sells Brazil nuts in a package that is a scale model of the building. The package is 5 inches high and has a square base that is 10 inches on each side. What is the volume of this container? Round your answer to two decimal places.

2. Rock salt, which is used to melt snow on highways in the north, is stored in cone-shaped buildings. This shape is used because it is the shape that a pile of salt forms as it is poured. A typical building measures 10 meters in diameter and has a height of 5 meters. What is the volume of rock salt that could be stored in such a building? Use 3.14 for π. Round your answer to two decimal places.

3. When corn is dumped into a pile, it naturally forms the shape of a cone. A pile of corn that is 60.8 feet in diameter and 12.9 feet high is in a farmer's field. How many cubic feet of corn are in the pile? Use 3.14 for π. Round your answer to two decimal places.

4. A company makes pyramid-shaped gift boxes in two sizes. The small size has a square base that is 3.5 inches by 3.5 inches and is 3.5 inches high. The large size has a square base that is 7 inches by 7 inches and is 6 inches high. What is the volume of each box? Round each answer to two decimal places.

5. Which has a greater volume, a cone with a height of 10 inches and a diameter of 5 inches, or a square pyramid with a height of 10 inches and a side length of 5 inches? Use 3.14 for π. Show your work and round your answers to two decimal places. Explain your answer using a complete sentence.

12

Name _____ Date _____

What on Earth?
Volumes and Surface Areas of Spheres

1. Assume that each planet is a sphere. Find the volume and surface area of each planet.
    Use 3.14 for π.   Round your answer to the nearest whole number.

Planet Name	Diameter (miles)	Volume (cubic miles)	Surface Area (square miles)
Mercury	3032		
Venus	7519		
Mars	4194		
Jupiter	88,736		
Saturn	74,978		
Uranus	32,193		
Neptune	30,775		
Pluto	1423		

2. The Carnegie Candy Company wants to make a spherical candy container with a surface area in
    square inches that is numerically equal to its volume in cubic inches. What must the radius of
    the sphere be? Use 3.14 for π. Round your answer to two decimal places.   Show your work
    and write your answer using a complete sentence.

Radius	Surface Area (square inches)	Volume (cubic inches)
1 inch	12.56	4.19
2 inches	50.24	33.49
3 inches	113.04	113.04

Assignment

Name _____ Date _____

Engineers and Architects
Nets and Views

Name the solid that is created when each net is folded.

1.

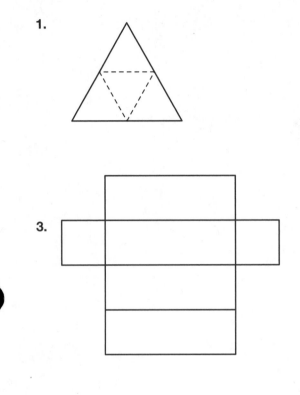

2.

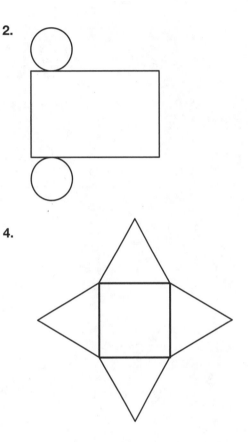

3.

4.

5.

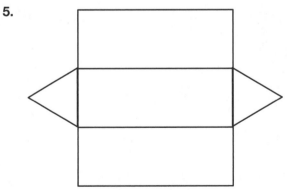

Assignment

© 2005 Carnegie Learning, Inc.

Name _____ Date _____

Double Take
Similar Solids

1. A tiger shark and a nurse shark are similar shapes. The tiger shark can grow to 12 feet in length, but the nurse shark will only grow to about 6 feet in length. A 12-foot long tiger shark could weigh 680 pounds. How much would a 6-foot nurse shark be expected to weigh? Write your answer using a complete sentence.

2. Pumpkins vary tremendously in size. If a 6-inch diameter pumpkin weighs 3 pounds, how much would you expect a pumpkin to weigh that is a similar shape but 3 feet in diameter? Write your answer using a complete sentence.

3. How many cubic feet are there in a cubic yard? (Hint: a cubic yard is the units of volume of a cube measuring 1 yard on each edge.) Write your answer using a complete sentence.

12

4. How many cubic inches are there in 1 cubic foot? Write your answer using a complete sentence.

5. The most popular size of model train is made so that everything is $\frac{1}{87}$ the size of the actual train.

   For example, a train car that measures 87 feet in real life would measure 1 foot in the model train. Find the volume of an actual train car that is 87 feet by 8 feet by 12 feet. Then find the volume of the model train car. Write your answer using a complete sentence. Round your answer to three decimal places.

6. A jet fuel tanker truck has a volume of 535 cubic feet. The company that makes the fuel is making a $\frac{1}{32}$ size model tanker truck to sell as a toy. What is the volume of the model truck in cubic feet? Round your answer to three decimal places. Write your answer using a complete sentence.

Assignment

Name _____   Date _____

Running a Tree Farm   Relations and Functions

In December of each year, you sell holiday trees raised on your tree farm. You sell your trees for $40 each for any size. You have $30 in your cash box as you begin Selling on a Saturday morning.

1. Complete the first four rows of the input-output table. The first row is done for you.

2. Write an algebraic expression to represent the amount of money you have in your cash box. Let x represent the number of trees sold.

Number of trees sold		Amount of money in cash drawer (dollars)
1	40(1) + 30	70
2		
3		
4		
		510
.	40(25) + 2030	1030

3. Find the number of trees that you would have sold if you have $510 in the drawer at the end of the day. Complete Row 5 of the table.

4. Find the number of trees that you would have sold if you have $1030 in the drawer at the end of the day. Complete Row 6 of the table.

5. Find the number of trees that you would have sold if you have $510 in the drawer at the end of the day. Complete Row 5 of the table.

6. Is the relation $y = 40x + 30$ a function? Write a complete sentence to explain why or why not

7. If the relation $y = 40x + 30$ is a function, identify the dependent variable and the independent variable. Write your answer using a complete sentence.

8. If relation $y = 40x + 30$ is a function, identify its domain and its range.

Find the value of each of function when $x = 12$.

9. $f(x) = 10x$

10. $f(x) = x - 2$

11. $f(x) = 100 - x$

12. $f(x) = x \div 2$

Assignment

Name _____ Date _____

Scaling a Cliff   Linear Functions

You finally make it to the top of the cliff, which is a height of 138 feet. You know that you can repel down the cliff at a rate of 3 feet per second.

1. How high are you from the ground after 1 second? Add this answer to the table.

2. How high are you from the ground after 2 seconds? Add this answer to the table.

3. How high are you from the ground after 3 seconds? Add this answer to the table.

4. Label the quantity names and units in both columns.

5. Label the Expression row in Column 1 as "*x.*" Then write an expression that will represent the quantity in Column 2 in terms of Column 1. Add this expression to the table.

	Column 1	Column 2
Quantity Name	Time	Height
Unit of Measure	seconds	feet
	1	
	2	
	3	
		108
Expression		

6. How many seconds will have passed when you are 108 feet above the ground? Add this answer to the table.

7. How many seconds will have passed when you are half-way down the cliff? Add the height and you answer to the table.

8. Write each row in the table as an ordered pair. Then graph the ordered pairs. Be sure that you place the independent variable on the horizontal axis. Draw a line through the ordered pairs.

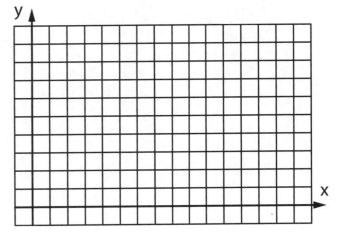

Assignment

Name _____ Date _____

Biking Along   Slope and Rates of Change

You start to save money for your next bike trip that you think will cost around $550. Your Uncle Lance gives you $100 to start your account. You plan to save $15 of your weekly allowance for the trip.

1. How much money will you have in 2 weeks? Add this answer to the table.

2. How much money will you have in 4 weeks? Add this answer to the table.

3. How much money will you have in 6 weeks? Add this answer to the table.

4. Label the quantity names and units in both columns.

5. Define a variable for the quantity in for Column 1 and add it to the table. Then write an expression to represent the amount in Column 2 in terms of the quantity in Column 1. Add this expression to the table.

13

	Column 1	Column 2
Quantity Name	Time	Money
Unit of Measure	weeks	dollars
	2	130
	4	160
	6	190
		325
		550
Expression		

6. Use the expression to determine the number of weeks that it will take to have $325 in your account. Add this answer to the table.

7. How many weeks will it take until you reach your goal? Add this answer to the table.

8. Write each row in the table as an ordered pair. Then graph the ordered pairs. Draw a line through the ordered pairs.

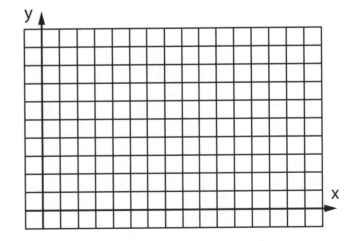

9. Use the graph to find the slope of the line.

Assignment

Name _____ Date _____

Let's Have a Pool Party! Finding Slope and *y*-Intercepts

At the beginning of the swimming season, you buy a 75-pound container of chlorine to keep your pool clean. You find that you are using 3 pounds of chlorine per week to keep your pool water sparkling clean.

1. How much chlorine is left after 2 weeks? Add this answer to the table.

2. How much chlorine is left after 10 weeks? Add this answer to the table.

3. How much chlorine is left after 15 weeks? Add this answer to the table.

4. Label the quantity names and units in both columns.

5. Define a variable for the quantity in for Column 1 and add it to the table. Then write an expression to represent the amount in Column 2 in terms of the quantity in Column 1. Add this expression to the table.

	Column 1	Column 2
	Time	Chlorine Remaining
Quantity Name	Time	Chlorine Remaining
Unit of Measure	weeks	pounds
	2	69
	10	45
	15	30
		21
		0
Expression		

6. Use the expression to determine the number of weeks until there are 21 pounds of chlorine left. Add this answer to the table.

7. How many weeks will it be until the chlorine is gone? Add this answer to the table.

8. Create a graph of the values in the table.

9. Use the graph to determine the *x*-intercept and the *y*-intercept.

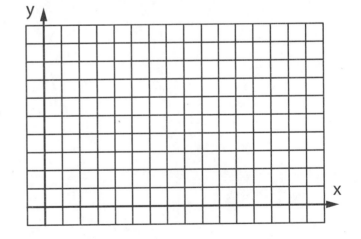

10. 10. Choose two points on the graph to find the slope.

Assignment

Name _____ Date _____

What's for Lunch? Using Slope and Intercepts to Graph Lines

You and your friends decide to go to Pete's Pizzeria for lunch. Pete charges $12 for the lunchtime special pizza

1. Write a linear function that models the total amount that you would pay if you ordered any number of pizzas.

2. What is the slope of this function? Write your answer using a complete sentence.

3. What is the *x*-intercept and what is the *y*-intercept? Write your answer using a complete sentence.

4. Complete the table to find the cost of buying the given number of pizzas.

x	y
1	
3	
5	
7	

5. Graph the function using the values in the table, the intercepts, and the slope.

Use the slope and the intercepts to graph each function.

$y = 10 - 5x$

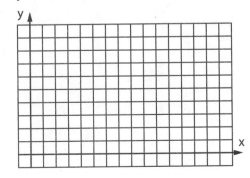

$y = 2x + 1$

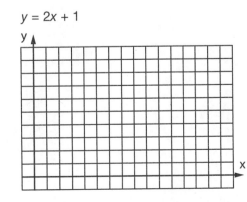

Assignment

Healthy Relationships Finding Lines of Best Fit

You and your classmates want to find out if there are any other relationships similar to the height to arm span relationship. You decide to see if there is a correlation between total height and the height from the floor to your navel! You collect data on several classmates.

Total Height (inches)	Height of Navel (inches)	Ratio of Navel Height to Total Height
67	41	1.63
77	48	
61	38	
73	45	
65	41	
53	33	
70	42	
74	46	
50	31	
63	41	

1. Complete the ratio column of the table. Round your answer to two decimal places. The first one is done for you.

2. Plot the ordered pairs in the table using the grid below. Label the horizontal axis as "Total Height (inches)" and the vertical axis as "Height of Navel (inches)." Number each axis in intervals of 5.

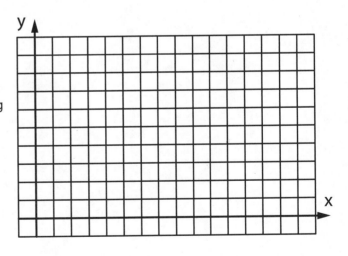

3. Decide what type of correlation, if any, that the data has. If there is a correlation, draw a line of best fit.

4. Write an equation of the line of best fit. Use your graph and the table to help you.

13

Name _____ Date _____

Is It a Bird or a Plane? Rational Numbers

Complete the table below by putting a dot in the boxes that describe each number or the result of the operation. The first one is completed for you.

Number	Natural Number	Whole Number	Integer	Rational Number
–8			●	●
2				
0				
4,238,399				
0.5				
12/17				
–14				
–13.46				
2.5 × 4				
4.5 + 3.5 – 8				
12 ÷ (–6)				
1.25 + 3.75				
2^{25}				
0.33...				

14

Name _____ Date _____

How Many Times? Powers of Rational Numbers

Find the value of each product of a power or quotient of a power.

1. $\left(\dfrac{2}{3}\right)^2\left(\dfrac{2}{3}\right)^4 =$

2. $(5)^4\,(5)^6 =$

3. $(4)^{-7}\,(4)^5 =$

4. $\dfrac{(3)^{-4}}{(3)^{-6}} =$

5. $\dfrac{\left(\dfrac{2}{3}\right)^{-3}}{\left(\dfrac{2}{3}\right)^{-3}} =$

6. $\dfrac{(2)^{14}}{(2)^{13}} =$

7. $10^{23} \div 10^{19} =$

8. $10^2 \times 10^{-6} =$

9. $10^{-4} \div 10^7 =$

10. $\dfrac{10^{17}}{10^{17}} =$

Name _____ Date _____

Sew What? Irrational Numbers

Identify the following as rational or irrational. Write a complete sentence to explain your answer.

1. 1. 1.2121…

2. 2. 0.313113111…

3. $\dfrac{25}{7}$

4. 123

5. $\sqrt{7}$

6. $\sqrt{(8+1)}$

7. 0.0123456789101112…

8. 0.33…

9. $\sqrt{3^2}$

Assignment

Name _____ Date _____

Worth 1000 Words Real Number and Their Properties

Decide whether each statement is true or false. Write a complete sentence to explain your reasoning.

1. A rational number is never a whole number.

2. An integer is always a whole number.

3. All whole numbers are rational numbers.

4. A square of a number is always a rational number.

5. All whole numbers are natural numbers.

For each statement, identify the property that the statement represents.

6. $12 + 4 = 4 + 12$

7. $-3 + (7 + 2) = (-3 + 7) + 2$

8. $1 \times (a + c) = (a + c)$

9. $17.356 + (-17.356) = 0$

10. $\dfrac{2}{3} \times \dfrac{3}{2} = 1$

11. $2 \times (8 \times 5) = 2 \times (5 \times 8)$

14

Name _____ Date _____

The House that Math Built The Distributive Property

Write an expression that will give the area of each region shown below.

1.

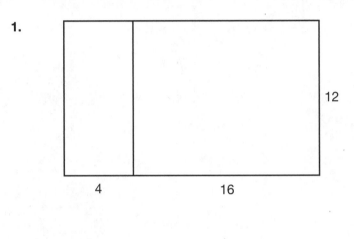

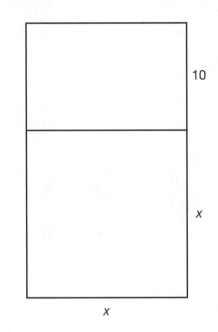

14

2. Identify the property that is used in each step of the solution below.

$$5(m + 3) = \frac{58 + 6m}{2}$$

$$5m + 15 = \frac{58 + 6m}{2}$$

$$5m + 15 = 29 + 3m$$

$$5m + 15 - 3m = 29 + 3m - 3m$$

$$2m + 15 = 29$$

$$2m + 15 - 15 = 29 - 15$$

$$2m = 14$$

$$2m\left(\frac{1}{2}\right) = 14\left(\frac{1}{2}\right)$$

$$m = 7$$

Assignment

Name _____ Date _____

Worms and Ants Graphing in Four Quadrants

1. Write the rows in the table as ordered pairs. Then graph the ordered pairs and draw a line though the points. Find the slope, intercepts, and equation of the line.

x-coordinate	y-coordinate
–4	1
–2	2
0	3
2	4
4	5

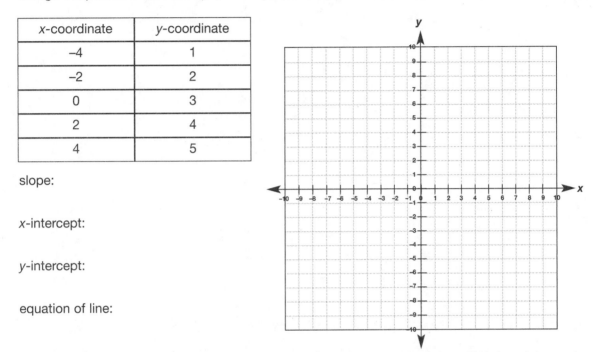

slope:

x-intercept:

y-intercept:

equation of line:

2. For the linear function $y = 3x - 4$, find the slope and the x- and y-intercepts. Plot the x-intercept and the y-intercept. Beginning at the y-intercept, use the slope to find another point on the line. Finally, draw a line through the points.

slope:

x-intercept:

y-intercept:

Assignment

Name _____ Date _____

Maps and Models Scale Drawings and Scale Models

The nickname of Nashville, Tennessee is "The Athens of the South" because of its long commitment to education. The town even constructed an exact replica of the Parthenon for the Centennial Exposition of 1879. In 1982, the construction began on Athena Parthenos, which stands 41 feet 10 inches tall.

1. The sculptor first made a 1:10 model from clay. This means that 1 inch on the model is equal to 10 inches in the real statue. What was the height of the clay model?

2. Later the sculptor made a 1:5 model. This means that 1 inch on the model is equal to 5 inches in the real statue. What was the height of the model?

3. You want to go with your friend to visit the Parthenon in Nashville. You are staying in down town Nashville. The scale on the map is 1 centimeter is equal to 1 kilometer. Use the scale to determine about the number of kilometers between Centennial Park where the Parthenon is located and your downtown hotel.

15

4. The table below shows the approximate distances between places in and around Nashville, Tennessee. Complete the table to show how far apart the places would be on a map using a scale of 1 cm = 1 km.

From	To	Actual Distance	Distance Apart on a Map (scale: 1 cm =1 km)
Downtown	Brooklyn Heights	4.5 km	
John C. Tume Airport	Downtown	10 km	
Downtown	Centennial Park	6.3 km	
Bordeaux Hills	West Nashville	2.5 km	

Assignment

Name _____ Date _____

What on Earth? Volumes and Surface Areas of Spheres

1. On the grid at the right, draw a triangle with vertices at (3, 3), (3, 7), and (6, 7). Label the triangle with the letter A.

2. Translate the triangle –10 units vertically. Label the new triangle with the letter B.

3. Translate triangle B –9 units horizontally. Label the new triangle with the letter C.

4. Translate triangle C 10 units vertically. Label the new triangle with the letter D.

5. Describe a translation that would map triangle A onto triangle D. Write your answer using a complete sentence.

6. The figure below has been rotated to a new position. Describe the transformation.

   The triangle was rotated _____degrees about the origin.

   Was the direction of rotation clockwise or counterclockwise?

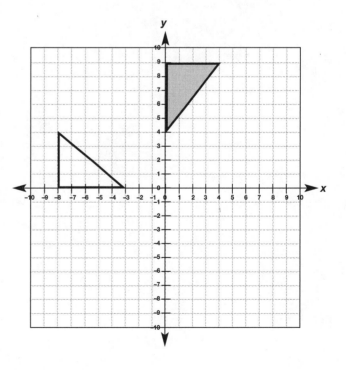

15

Assignment

Name _____ Date _____

Secret Codes Flipping, Stretching, and Shrinking

1. Record the coordinates of the vertices of the hexagon in the table below.

2. Reflect the hexagon in the y-axis. Record the ordered pairs of the image in the table below.

3. Reflect the original hexagon in the x-axis. Record the ordered pairs of the image in the table below.

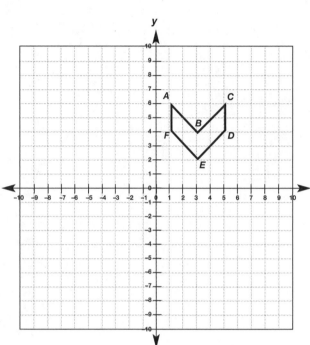

Pre-image	Image 1	Image 2
A		
B		
C		
D		
E		
F		

4. Dilate the rectangle *FACE* by a scale factor of 2 using the origin as the center of dilation. Label the vertices of the image.

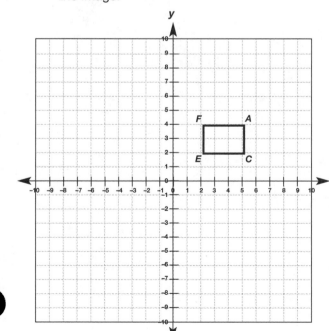

5. Reflect the word MOM in the y-axis. Is it still a word?

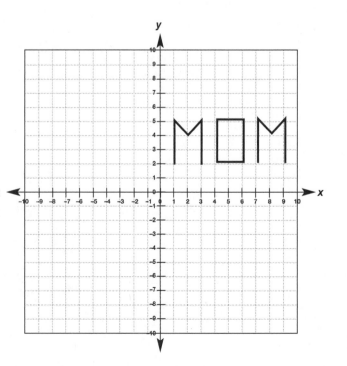

Assignment

Name _____ Date _____

A Stitch in Time Multiple Transformations

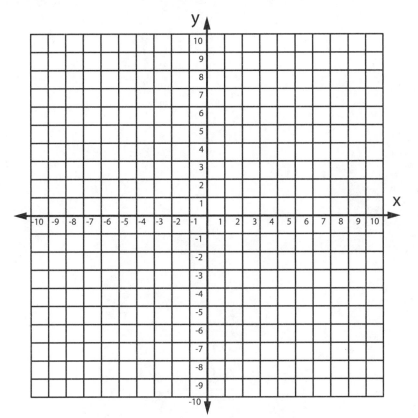

15

1. On the grid above, draw a quadrilateral with vertices at (2, 2), (3, 5), (7, 5) and (4, 2). Label the quadrilateral with the letter A.

2. Reflect the quadrilateral in the *x*-axis. Label the new quadrilateral with the letter B.

3. Rotate quadrilateral B 180 degrees about the origin. Label the new quadrilateral with the letter C.

4. Reflect quadrilateral C over the *x*-axis. Label the new quadrilateral with the letter D.

5. Describe a transformation that would map quadrilateral A onto quadrilateral D. Write your answer using a complete sentence.

Skills Practice

Name _____ Date _____

Reflect & Review

1. Jack and Pablo are looking for summer jobs. Jack finds a job that pays $7.25 per hour and guarantees 30 hours per week. Pablo finds a job that pays $8.35 per hour and guarantees 25 hours per week. Find the earnings per week for each boy.

2. Sam collected monetary donations for the food pantry last week. He collected $372.31 from the freshman class, $231.44 from the sophomore class, $543.87 from the junior class and $632.22 from the senior class. How much money did Sam collect for the food pantry?

3. Use mental math to find the sum: 40 + 38.

4. Estimate the product of 450 and 820.

5. Ice cream costs $3.55 per gallon. How much does 5 gallons of ice cream cost?

Practice

Perform the indicated operations.

6. $(4 + 13) - (7 + 2)$

7. $6 \bullet 4 + 1 - 5$

8. $8 + 27 \div 3$

9. $4 \bullet 3 + 6$

10. $15 \div 5 + 14 - 8$

11. $9 - 3 \bullet 2 + 6$

Decide where to place the parentheses so that the answer is correct using the order of operations.

12. $14 + 7 \div 3 + 8 = 15$

13. $9 - 6 + 2 \div 2 = 5$

Name _____ Date _____

1. You bought four 3-ring binders for $14. How much does one 3-ring binder cost?

2. Piper is making oatmeal raisin cookies for your class party. One batch of the recipe she is using makes 24 cookies. If Piper makes 3 batches of the recipe, how many cookies will she have made?

3. You purchased 5 DVDs for $15.99 and 6 video game cartridges for $35.99. What is the total cost of your purchase?

4. Use mental math to find the product: $20 \cdot 161$.   5. Simplify: $7 + 12 \div 6 - 2 \cdot 3$.

1

Practice

List all of the factor pairs of each number.

6. 30   7. 27

8. 42   9. 31

10. Is 3 a factor of 57? Justify your answer.   11. Is 4 a factor of 64? Justify your answer.

12. Is 7 a factor of 98? Justify your answer.   13. Is 5 a factor of 33? Justify your answer.

List all of the factors of each number in each pair. Then circle the factors that the numbers have in common.

14. 12, 15   15. 24, 36

List the first five multiples of each number.

16. 15   17. 40

Skills Practice

Name _____ Date _____

1. One-third of your class of 18 students likes vanilla ice cream. How many students in your class like vanilla ice cream?

2. Your teacher is rearranging 24 desks in a classroom. He wants the same number of desks in each row. Find all possible rectangular arrangements that have no more than 10 desks in any row or column.

3. A museum is displaying a 54-piece coin collection in groups so that the same number of coins is in each group. List the different ways in which the coins can be displayed.

4. Write all of the factors of 45

5. Simplify: $4 + 3 \cdot 6 - 8 \div 2$

Practice

6. List the first eight multiples of 2.

7. List the first ten multiples of 5.

8. List the first ten multiples of 3 and 4. Circle the multiples that 3 and 4 have in common.

9. List the first eight multiples of 6 and 8. Circle the multiples that 6 and 8 have in common.

10. Is 42 a multiple of 4? Justify your answer.

11. Is 63 a multiple of 7? Justify your answer.

Find the least common multiple of each pair of numbers.

12. 15, 25

13. 12, 16

14. 27, 36

Name _____ Date _____

Reflect & Review

1. You run 2 miles every third day and swim every Wednesday. Today you are going to run and swim. In how many days will you run and swim on the same day?

2. You are balancing your checkbook. The beginning balance is $64.32. You have written checks for $11.08, $4.82, and $15.91. What is the ending balance of your checkbook?

3. Use mental math to find the product: $67 \cdot 40$.

4. Demonstrate the commutative property of multiplication using the numbers 7 and 15.

5. Decide where to place parentheses so that the statement is true.

$24 - 12 + 3 + 8 - 2 = 15$.

Practice

6. Is the number 54 prime or composite? Justify your answer.

7. List the next three prime numbers after 7.

8. True or False: All odd numbers are prime. Justify your answer.

9. True or False. All even numbers are composite. Justify your answer.

10. Is the number 37 prime or composite? Justify.

11. List all of the prime numbers between 20 and 30.

12. List all of the prime numbers between 40 and 60.

Skills Practice

Name _____ Date _____

Reflect & Review

1. A rectangular gymnasium floor needs to be refinished. If the floor is 90 feet wide and 128 feet long, what is the area that will be refinished?

2. Paul has $0.88 in change. He wants you to guess which coins he has. He tells you that you need to use the least amount of coins possible. What coins does Paul have?

3. List the next three prime numbers after 31.   **4.** Find the least common multiple of 18 and 27.

Practice

Construct a factor tree for each number. Then write the prime factorization of each number.

5. 27   **6.** 100   **7.** 35

8. 98   **9.** 24   **10.** 36

Determine where to place parentheses so that the statement properly demonstrates the associative property.

11. $(4 \bullet 5) \bullet 8 = 4 \bullet 5 \bullet 8$ **12.** $3 \bullet (10 \bullet 2) = 3 \bullet 10 \bullet 2$

Skills Practice

Name _____ Date _____

Reflect & Review

1. Three-fifths of the 1065 students in your school want pizza for lunch. How many students in your school do not want pizza?

2. You are selling candy bars to raise money for a class trip. One candy bar sells for $1.50. You have to sell enough candy bars to raise $129. How many candy bars do you have to sell?

3. Your friend asks you to explain the difference between prime and composite numbers. Use complete sentences in your explanation.

4. Use a factor tree to find the prime factorization of 48.

5. Find the least common multiple of 12 and 20.

Practice

Identify the base and exponent in the power.

6. 5^8

7. 2^3

Write the product as a power.

8. $4 \cdot 4 \cdot 4 \cdot 4 \cdot 4$

9. $3 \cdot 3 \cdot 3 \cdot 3 \cdot 3 \cdot 3 \cdot 3$

Write the prime factorization of the number using powers.

10. 28

11. 36

12. 125

13. 200

Skills Practice

Name _____ Date _____

Reflect & Review

1. An art store is displaying small pieces of art on a wall. There are 18 pieces. How many different ways could the art be displayed with an equal amount of paintings in each row?

2. Your summer job is mowing lawns. If you earn $30 per yard mowed, how many days will it take you to save $540?

3. Write the prime factorization of the number 400 using powers.

4. Use mental math to find the product: 18 • 600.

5. Is the number 273 prime or composite? Justify your answer.

Practice

6. What is the difference between the greatest common factor and least common multiple of a pair of numbers?

Find the greatest common factor of the numbers.

7. 12 and 15

8. 20 and 30

9. 8 and 12

10. 42 and 54

11. 49 and 63

12. 80 and 64

13. 25 and 40

14. 48 and 72

Skills Practice

Name _____ Date _____

Reflect & Review

1. You and your friends have $18 for lunch. You buy three sandwiches for $4 each and three drinks for $1 each. Assuming that the tax has already been included, do you have enough to pay for your lunch? Show your work.

2. This summer, you earned $1920 in 12 weeks. How much money did you earn each week?

3. What are the factors of 64?

4. Use mental math to find the quotient: $1200 \div 60$.

Practice

5. Identify the numerator of the fraction: $\dfrac{3}{8}$.   6. Identify the denominator of the fraction: $\dfrac{15}{44}$.

7. Write the fraction that has a numerator of 10 and a denominator of 19.

8. Write the fraction that has a denominator of 11 and a numerator of 5.

Complete the each statement.

9. $\dfrac{1}{6}$ is the same as $\dfrac{1}{12}$ s.   10. $\dfrac{4}{9}$ is the same as $\dfrac{1}{18}$ s.   11. $\dfrac{1}{5}$ is the same as $\dfrac{1}{25}$ s.

Represent each fraction using the specified figure.

12. $\dfrac{4}{5}$ of a circle   13. $\dfrac{1}{4}$ of a rectangle   14. $\dfrac{7}{9}$ of a square

Skills Practice

Name _____ Date _____

Reflect & Review

1. You are reading a book for English class and you figure that you can read 15 pages in an hour. The book is 345 pages. How long will it take you to read the book?

2. Seth wants to build a fence to enclose his back yard. The area to fence has three sides with measurements of 25 feet, 75 feet, and 27feet. If the fencing that Seth chooses costs $5 per panel, how much would it cost him to fence his backyard? (A panel is 4 feet in length and partial panels cannot be purchased.)

3. Use parentheses to make the sentence true.

   $4 \cdot 6 + 16 \div 5 + 3 = 26$

4. Write a fraction with the numerator of 18 and denominator of 33.

Practice

5. Three submarine sandwiches need to be divided equally among 5 people. How much of a sandwich does each person get?

6. You and three of your friends have 3 bags of jewelry beads that you are dividing equally among all of you. How much of a bag does each person get?

Determine whether the following solution is reasonable. Use complete sentences to explain why or why not.

7. In celebration of Pie Day (March 14 for 3.14), your math teacher bought 17 pizza pies. Each pizza is cut into 6 slices. There are 30 students in your class. Each student will receive 5 slices of pizza.

Name _____ Date _____

1. Max is baking cookies. His makes 24 cookies from his first batch and 32 cookies from his second batch. He wants to divide the cookies equally into 8 boxes. How many cookies go in each box?

2. Find the greatest common factor of 15 and 40.

3. Write 6 • 6 • 7 • 7 • 7 using powers.

4. Jillian wants to purchase a new MP3 player that is priced at $125. She earns $25 each week working after school at a library. How many weeks will it take Jillian to save for the MP3 player?

The lunch menu at your school offers three main dishes: hamburger, hot dog, or pizza. As the freshman class went through the line, 24 students chose a hamburger, 33 students chose a hotdog, and 47 students chose pizza.

5. What fraction chose a hamburger?

6. What fraction chose a hotdog?

7. What fraction did not choose a hot dog?

8. There are 47 students in Lilly's gym class. Fifteen students in the class prefer volleyball, 28 students prefer track, and 4 students prefer football. What fraction of the students prefers volleyball and football?

One hundred twenty-two thousand people applied for football season tickets at a state university. Forty-four thousand three hundred twenty-one applications got donor-seat tickets, 67,493 got regular-seat tickets, and the remaining did not get tickets.

9. What fraction got donor-seat tickets?

10. What fraction got regular-seat tickets ?

Skills Practice

Name _____ Date _____

1. Lonnie and Dana are practicing for a free throw contest. Both shoot 20 free throws. Dana makes 17 and Lonnie makes 14. What fraction of the throws did each person make?

2. Find the greatest common factor of 8 and 18.

3. Use mental math to find the product: $25 \cdot 40$.

4. You and three of your friends go to the water park. One admission to the water park is $15. What is the total cost for all of you to go to the water park?

2

Practice

Fill in the blank so that each pair of fractions are equivalent.

5. $\dfrac{2}{5} = \dfrac{6}{\underline{}}$

6. $\dfrac{5}{8} = \dfrac{25}{\underline{}}$

7. $\dfrac{3}{4} = \dfrac{12}{\underline{}}$

8. $\dfrac{7}{10} = \dfrac{42}{\underline{}}$

9. $\dfrac{8}{9} = \dfrac{56}{\underline{}}$

10. $\dfrac{4}{7} = \dfrac{48}{\underline{}}$

Fill in the blanks so that each equality is true.

11. $\dfrac{1}{3} = \dfrac{1 \times }{3 \times } = \dfrac{7}{21}$

12. $\dfrac{4}{5} = \dfrac{4 \times }{5 \times } = \dfrac{12}{15}$

13. $\dfrac{9}{20} = \dfrac{9 \times }{20 \times } = \dfrac{36}{80}$

14. $\dfrac{5}{11} = \dfrac{5 \times }{11 \times } = \dfrac{25}{55}$

15. $\dfrac{8}{15} = \dfrac{8 \times }{15 \times } = \dfrac{48}{90}$

16. $\dfrac{7}{30} = \dfrac{7 \times }{30 \times } = \dfrac{49}{210}$

Name _____ Date _____

Reflect & Review

1. Heather is placing winning tickets under every third chair at the orchestra concert. The chairs are numbered and there are 300 chairs. As she was putting the tickets under the chairs, she became confused. She is at chair number 244 and wants to know if she should put a ticket under the chair. Should she put the ticket under the chair? Explain.

2. Use a factor tree to find the prime factorization for 81.

3. List the first 5 multiples of 5.

4. Find the greatest common factor of 6 and 10.

2

Practice

Fill in the blank(s) so that each equality is true.

5. $\dfrac{8}{10} = \dfrac{4}{}$

6. $\dfrac{15}{30} = \dfrac{}{2}$

7. $\dfrac{12}{15} = \dfrac{4}{}$

8. $\dfrac{32}{36} = \dfrac{32 \div }{36 \div } = \dfrac{8}{9}$

9. $\dfrac{21}{28} = \dfrac{21 \div }{28 \div } = \dfrac{3}{4}$

10. $\dfrac{18}{27} = \dfrac{18 \div }{27 \div } = \dfrac{2}{3}$

Simplify each fraction.

11. $\dfrac{20}{25}$

12. $\dfrac{8}{12}$

13. $\dfrac{35}{40}$

14. $\dfrac{24}{64}$

15. $\dfrac{18}{38}$

16. $\dfrac{26}{65}$

Skills Practice

Name _____ Date _____

1. At a garage sale, Wanda bought 4 books for $1 each, 2 CDs for $3 each and 3 toys for her baby sister for $2 each. How much money did Wanda spend?

2. During the first series of last night's football game, the quarterback ran for 8 yards, was sacked for 4 yards, and threw a pass for 5 yards. To earn a first down, ten yards must be gained. Did they earn a first down? Justify your answer.

3. Simplify: $\dfrac{36}{81}$.

4. Use mental math to find the product: 200 • 42.

2

Practice

Use your knowledge of common fractions to compare each pair of fractions.

5. $\dfrac{3}{8}$, $\dfrac{3}{4}$

6. $\dfrac{7}{10}$, $\dfrac{5}{14}$

Find the LCD of each pair of fractions. Then use the LCD to rewrite each fraction. Circle the original fraction that is greater.

7. $\dfrac{4}{5}$, $\dfrac{7}{15}$

8. $\dfrac{2}{7}$, $\dfrac{1}{5}$

9. $\dfrac{5}{6}$, $\dfrac{7}{9}$

10. $\dfrac{1}{3}$, $\dfrac{2}{5}$

11. $\dfrac{1}{2}$, $\dfrac{4}{7}$

12. $\dfrac{3}{8}$, $\dfrac{4}{9}$

Name _____ Date _____

1. You are training for a marathon. The first week of training you need to run at least 42 miles in 6 days. If you run the same number of miles each day for the 6 days, how many miles do you have to run each day?

2. Your friend Louie tells you that any positive number multiplied by 2 is a composite number. Is he correct? Justify your answer.

3. Order the following fractions from least to greatest: $\dfrac{2}{3}$, $\dfrac{4}{9}$, $\dfrac{1}{2}$, $\dfrac{7}{8}$, $\dfrac{1}{12}$, $\dfrac{13}{14}$.

4. Find the greatest common factor of 27 and 36.

5. Find the least common multiple of 12 and 16.

Perform the indicated operation(s). Simplify your answer, if possible.

6. $\dfrac{3}{5} + \dfrac{1}{5}$

7. $\dfrac{1}{7} + \dfrac{2}{7} + \dfrac{3}{7}$

8. $\dfrac{3}{16} + \dfrac{1}{16} + \dfrac{5}{16}$

6. $\dfrac{4}{9} - \dfrac{3}{9}$

7. $\dfrac{10}{11} - \dfrac{4}{11}$

8. $\dfrac{4}{15} + \dfrac{1}{15}$

6. $\dfrac{14}{17} - \dfrac{11}{17}$

7. $\dfrac{7}{10} - \dfrac{3}{10}$

8. $\dfrac{4}{7} + \dfrac{6}{7} - \dfrac{3}{7}$

Name _____ Date _____

1. You have $\frac{3}{4}$ of a yard of material. You use a piece that is $\frac{1}{4}$ of a yard long for one pillow. How much fabric do you have left? Simplify your answer, if possible.

2. The U.S. Mint is issuing new state quarters. There is one state quarter for each of the 50 states. If you collect all 50 quarters and want to display them in a rectangular display with the same number of quarters in each row, how many ways can you arrange the quarters?

3. Find the least common multiple of 9 and 15.

4. Write the prime factorization of the number 56 using powers.

Practice

Perform the indicated operation(s). Simplify your answer, if possible.

5. $\frac{1}{4} + \frac{1}{2}$

6. $\frac{1}{7} + \frac{5}{14}$

7. $\frac{3}{16} + \frac{1}{8} + \frac{1}{16}$

8. $\frac{5}{6} - \frac{1}{3}$

9. $\frac{5}{12} - \frac{7}{24}$

10. $\frac{2}{3} + \frac{1}{15}$

11. $\frac{4}{7} + \frac{9}{14} - \frac{1}{2}$

12. $\frac{3}{8} - \frac{1}{4} + \frac{9}{16}$

13. $\frac{4}{15} + \frac{1}{3} - \frac{1}{5}$

Name _____ Date _____

Reflect & Review

1. A bakery sells cookies for $1 each and slices of pie for $3 each. If the bakery sells 44 cookies and 15 slices of pie, how much money did the bakery make from the cookies and pie?

2. Find the perimeter of the rectangle. Hint: perimeter = 2 length + 2 width

3. Simplify the expression: $7 \cdot 3 + 6 - 2 \cdot 8 \div 4$.

9 in.

17 in.

4. Find the sum of 4^2 and 3^3.

3

Practice

Write each mixed number as an improper fraction.

5. $6\dfrac{1}{2}$

6. $1\dfrac{5}{8}$

7. $3\dfrac{1}{8}$

Write each improper fraction as a mixed number.

8. $\dfrac{11}{3}$

9. $\dfrac{15}{7}$

10. $\dfrac{23}{6}$

11. $\dfrac{19}{2}$

12. $\dfrac{13}{4}$

13. $\dfrac{19}{5}$

Find the sum. Simplify your answer, if possible.

14. $\dfrac{3}{5} + \dfrac{3}{5}$

15. $\dfrac{7}{9} + \dfrac{4}{9}$

16. $\dfrac{2}{3} + \dfrac{5}{4}$

Name _____ Date _____

Reflect & Review

1. You are making gift bags for a third grade class. You have 56 mini candy bars, 14 bouncy balls, and 70 pieces of gum. What is the greatest number of identical gift bags that you can make? How many of each item will be in each bag?

2. You want to buy a guitar that costs $1225. You have saved $550 and are earning $45 per week at your current after-school job. If you saved your earnings every week, how long will it take before you can buy the guitar?

3. Use mental math to find the product: $43 \cdot 8$. (Think $40 \cdot 8 + 3 \cdot 8$.)

4. Find the least common denominator of the fractions: $\dfrac{3}{7}$, $\dfrac{2}{5}$, $\dfrac{1}{2}$.

Practice

Find each product. Simplify your answer, if possible.

5. $\dfrac{3}{4} \times \dfrac{2}{9}$

6. $\dfrac{8}{15} \times \dfrac{1}{4}$

7. $\dfrac{4}{3} \times \dfrac{5}{6}$

8. $\dfrac{7}{10} \times \dfrac{6}{35}$

9. $\dfrac{7}{4} \times \dfrac{10}{21}$

10. $\dfrac{11}{12} \times \dfrac{16}{33}$

11. $\dfrac{15}{24} \times \dfrac{6}{20}$

12. $\dfrac{14}{35} \times \dfrac{10}{8}$

13. $\dfrac{9}{32} \times \dfrac{28}{33}$

Name _____ Date _____

1. There are 20 people running a 5-kilometer race. You have five oranges. If the oranges are evenly shared with the runners, how much of an orange should each runner get?

2. Find the area of the rectangle shown at the left. Hint: area = length x width

$\frac{4}{5}$ m

3. Write $\frac{16}{3}$ as a mixed number.

$\frac{2}{5}$ m

4. Write the prime factorization of 96 using a factor tree.

Find each quotient. Simplify your answer, if possible.

5. $\frac{15}{7} \div \frac{10}{14}$

6. $\frac{2}{9} \div \frac{4}{3}$

7. $\frac{11}{6} \div \frac{2}{7}$

8. $\frac{5}{8} \div \frac{25}{14}$

9. $\frac{14}{32} \div \frac{7}{8}$

10. $\frac{45}{33} \div \frac{15}{11}$

11. $\frac{10}{3} \div \frac{35}{27}$

12. $\frac{24}{5} \div \frac{26}{20}$

Name _____ Date _____

1. There are 24 students in your math class. If two-thirds of the students are girls, how many boys are in your math class?

2. What is $\dfrac{1}{2}$ of $\dfrac{2}{3}$?

3. Find the GCF of 14 and 28.

4. Is the number 43 prime or composite? Justify your answer.

3

Practice

Find each sum. Simplify your answer, if possible.

5. $3\dfrac{2}{5} + 6\dfrac{1}{5}$

6. $2\dfrac{5}{9} + 8\dfrac{2}{9}$

7. $4\dfrac{3}{8} + 1\dfrac{1}{4}$

8. $6\dfrac{4}{7} + 4\dfrac{3}{14}$

9. $3\dfrac{2}{9} + 5\dfrac{1}{3}$

10. $1\dfrac{1}{6} + 3\dfrac{2}{3}$

Find each difference. Simplify your answer, if possible.

11. $11\dfrac{11}{12} - 6\dfrac{7}{12}$

12. $5\dfrac{7}{8} - 1\dfrac{3}{8}$

13. $9\dfrac{11}{12} - 6\dfrac{7}{12}$

Skills Practice

Name _____ Date _____

Reflect & Review

1. Out of 20 questions on the quiz, you answered 15 of them correctly. What fraction did you answer correctly? Simplify your answer, if possible.

2. Use mental math to find the product: 14 x 280

3. Find the least common multiple of 12 and 8.

4. On day one of a camping trip, it rained $3 \frac{1}{4}$ inches. On day two, it rained $3 \frac{2}{3}$ inches. On the last day, it rained $\frac{5}{8}$ inches. What is the total amount of rainfall for the three days?

Practice

Find each product. Simplify your answer, if possible.

5. $2 \frac{1}{4} \times 1 \frac{7}{33}$

6. $3 \frac{3}{5} \times 7 \frac{1}{2}$

7. $2 \frac{5}{8} \times 6 \frac{2}{9}$

8. $1 \frac{19}{21} \times 2 \frac{4}{5}$

9. $2 \frac{1}{3} \times 3 \frac{3}{26}$

10. $2 \frac{3}{5} \times 7 \frac{5}{9}$

Find each quotient. Simplify your answer, if possible.

11. $3 \frac{9}{11} \div 1 \frac{7}{22}$

12. $4 \frac{2}{3} \div 1 \frac{13}{15}$

13. $4 \frac{4}{5} \div 1 \frac{11}{25}$

Skills Practice

Name _____ Date _____

Reflect & Review

1. A classroom measures $31\frac{1}{2}$ feet wide. If a desk and the space around it take up $5\frac{1}{4}$ feet, how many rows of desks will fit in the classroom?

2. Which fraction is greater $\frac{7}{9}$ or $\frac{3}{4}$?

3. Use mental math to find the product: 70 x 300.

4. You answered $\frac{17}{20}$ of the questions on a test correctly. If there were 100 questions on the test, how many did you answer correctly?

Practice

Complete each statement using the correct number of units. Show your work.

5. 5 inches =   feet

6. 2 tons =   pounds

7. 5 pints =   quarts

8. 72 feet =   yards

9. 7 gallons =   quarts

10. $2\frac{1}{2}$ pounds =   ounces

Complete the statement using <, >, or =. Show your work.

11. 8 feet   90 inches

12. 7 cups   2 quarts

Name _____ Date _____

Reflect & Review

1. Joe has been working on his homework all evening. He finished $\frac{3}{4}$ of his history project and $\frac{5}{8}$ of his English homework. For which class did he complete more work?

2. Find the perimeter of the triangle with sides that measure $\frac{6}{7}$ feet, $\frac{2}{3}$ feet, and $\frac{14}{21}$ feet.

3. Use mental math to find the product: 0.453 x 100.

4. Find the quotient: $\frac{9}{35} \div \frac{6}{7}$.

Practice

Complete each statement. Show your work.

5. 500 pennies =   dollars   6. 15 dimes =   half-dollars   7. 25 nickels =   quarters

8. Complete the statement by writing each digit as part of a dollar.

   $3.72 =   dollars + (7 x   of a dollar) + (2 x   of a dollar)

Complete each statement to write the decimal in a different form.

9. $18.96 =   tens +   ones +   tenths (   ) +   hundredths (   )

10. $573.17 =   hundreds +   tens +   ones +   tenths +   hundredths

11. $74.619 =   tens +   ones +   tenths +   hundredths +   thousandths

12. $94.013 =   tens +   ones +   tenths +   hundredths +   thousandths

13. $199.67 =   hundreds +   tens +   ones +   tenths +   hundredths

Skills Practice

Name _____ Date _____

1. Find the area of the rectangle shown.

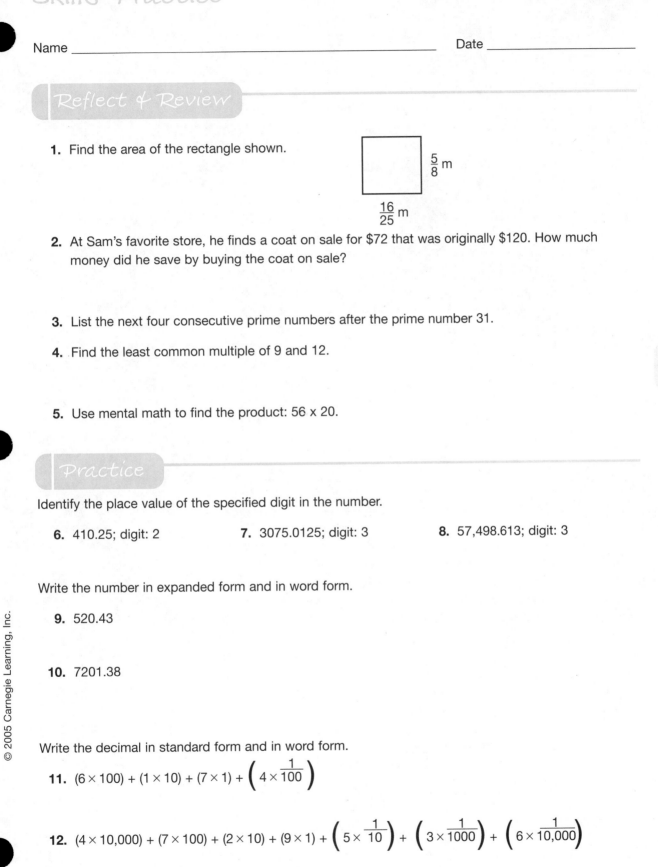

$\frac{5}{8}$ m

$\frac{16}{25}$ m

2. At Sam's favorite store, he finds a coat on sale for $72 that was originally $120. How much money did he save by buying the coat on sale?

3. List the next four consecutive prime numbers after the prime number 31.

4. Find the least common multiple of 9 and 12.

5. Use mental math to find the product: 56 x 20.

4

Practice

Identify the place value of the specified digit in the number.

6. 410.25; digit: 2

7. 3075.0125; digit: 3

8. 57,498.613; digit: 3

Write the number in expanded form and in word form.

9. 520.43

10. 7201.38

Write the decimal in standard form and in word form.

11. $(6 \times 100) + (1 \times 10) + (7 \times 1) + \left(4 \times \frac{1}{100} \right)$

12. $(4 \times 10,000) + (7 \times 100) + (2 \times 10) + (9 \times 1) + \left(5 \times \frac{1}{10} \right) + \left(3 \times \frac{1}{1000} \right) + \left(6 \times \frac{1}{10,000} \right)$

Name _____ Date _____

Reflect & Review

1. James and Ken are landscaping for a business in town. The drawing at the right represents the lawn. Find the area James and Ken will mow.

6 ft
8 ft
3 ft
17 ft

2. Tosin has worked $14\frac{1}{2}$ hours this week. Next week she wants to work 25 hours. How many more hours will she work next week than this week?

3. Find the value of the expression: $19 - 25 \div 5 + 7 - (18 - 20)$.

4. Simplify: $\frac{14}{35} \cdot \frac{15}{16} \div \frac{5}{4}$.

4

Practice

Write each decimal as a mixed number. Simplify your answer, if possible.

5. 21.04

6. 14.002

7. 200.205

Round each whole number to the given place value.

8. 5736 to the nearest ten

9. 84,521 to the nearest thousand

10. 244 to the nearest hundred

11. In the table, round each decimal to the given place value.

	Round to the nearest hundred	Round to the nearest ten	Round to the nearest one	Round to the nearest tenth	Round to the nearest hundredth	Round to the nearest thousandth
4735.1628						
258.0751						
632.9516						

Skills Practice

Name _____ Date _____

1. Your class has ordered 27 sub sandwiches. There are 24 students in your class. Your teacher has placed your class in groups of 4. How many sub sandwiches will each group receive? How much will each group member receive?

2. Order the numbers from least to greatest: 0.48, $\frac{1}{10}$, 0.85, $\frac{3}{4}$, $\frac{1}{2}$, $\frac{8}{10}$, 0.25

3. You are baking cookies and want to double the recipe. The recipe calls for $2\frac{1}{4}$ cups of flour and $\frac{3}{4}$ cup of sugar. What will the measurements of each ingredient be when you double the recipe?

4. Perform the indicated operations: $\frac{7}{4} + \frac{8}{3} - \frac{1}{2}$. Simplify your answer, if possible.

Practice

Find each sum or difference

5. 54.3 + 22.9

6. 10.326 + 62.931

7. 19.71 + 33.55

8. 64.67 − 14.15

9. 194.337 − 123.015

10. 22.6 − 10.2

11. 473.44 + 94.2

12. 78.321 − 39.7

13. 628.907 + 129.8

Skills Practice

Name _____ Date _____

Reflect & Review

1. Jessica is buying birthday presents for her twin nieces. She has $64 to spend. So far she has purchased two swimsuits for $12.50 each and two pairs of flip-flops for $4.63 each. She wants to buy each twin a basketball that costs $15.33. Does Jessica have enough money to purchase the basketballs?

2. Find the area of a triangle that has a height of 4 feet and a base of $6\frac{1}{2}$ feet.

   (Hint: Area = $\frac{1}{2}$ Base × Height)

3. Simplify: $\frac{15}{33} \times \frac{25}{55}$.

4. Find the greatest common factor of 24 and 56.

4

Practice

Find each product.

5. 3.2×2.01

6. 4.6×0.05

7. 5.04×1.03

8. 2.17×0.04

9. 7.34×1.6

10. 301.2×5.8

11. 8.4×10.3

12. 17.08×2.4

13. 11.3×0.07

Name _____ Date _____

1. Draw a circle. Use it to represent the fraction $\frac{7}{8}$.

2. Ten pizzas are divided evenly among 32 people. What fraction of a pizza does each person get? Justify your answer.

3. Simplify: $\frac{3}{16} + \frac{3}{4} - \frac{3}{8}$.

4. Find the product: $7\frac{3}{5} \times 2\frac{1}{2}$.

Find each quotient.

5. $8\overline{)46}$

6. $9\overline{)43.2}$

7. $4\overline{)9.52}$

8. $3.5\overline{)73.5}$

9. $0.2\overline{)8.36}$

10. $8\overline{)1.2}$

11. $0.98 \div 0.7$

12. $3.21 \div 0.3$

Skills Practice

Name _____ Date _____

Reflect & Review

1. Glennis runs 5.75 miles per week and swims 3.5 miles per week. How many miles of exercise does she get each week?

2. Shelly is traveling to her grandmother's house that is 324 miles away. If her car gets 23 miles per gallon, how many gallons of gasoline will she use on the trip?

3. Find the least common multiple of 18 and 24.

4. Write $8\frac{7}{9}$ as an improper fraction.

4

Practice

Convert each measure. Show all of your work.

5. 30 hectometers =   kilometers

6. 18 millimeters =   meters

7. 5.32 decimeters =   hectometers

8. 18.7 liters =   milliliters

9. 0.1 meters =   centimeters

10. 15 centiliters =   kiloliters

11. 3.2 milligrams =   grams

12. 0.09 kilograms =   centigrams

13. 15.5 decimeter =   kilometer

14. 3.67 millimeters =   centimeters

Name _____ Date _____

Reflect & Review

1. Gill wants a CD player that costs $135.49. The sales tax is $10.16. How much money does he need to purchase the CD player including tax?

2. Hannah wants to place a small fence border around her rectangular flower bed. The dimensions of the sides are 12.5 centimeters and 18.8 centimeters. How much fencing will she need?

3. Write 452.89 in expanded form.

4. Find the difference: 634.27 − 421.8.

5

Practice

Write each statement as a ratio in two ways, (a) as a fraction and (b) using a colon.

5. Thirteen out of twenty boys like football.

6. Sue answered 19 out of 25 questions correctly.

7. Jake made 12 out of 18 putts on the golf course.

8. Pat ate 3 out of 8 pieces of pizza.

9. Kevin made 15 baskets out of 26 attempts at the basketball game.

10. Matt threw 30 strikes out of 43 pitches. How many pitches were not strikes?

11. Phil caught one out of every three passes. How many passes did he miss?

12. Ingra answered 12 out of 20 phone calls. How many phone calls did she miss?

Name _____   Date _____

Reflect & Review

1. Kathy enjoys working in her vegetable garden. She wants to hire you to water the plants while she is out of town for the weekend. She waters each section for $\frac{1}{3}$ hour. There are 15 sections that need to be watered. Kathy offers to pay you $5 per hour. How much will you make?

2. Ty is selling programs at the hockey game. For every program he sells, $0.25 goes to the Children's Hospital. If he sells 435 programs, how much money will the Children's Hospital receive?

3. Use mental math to simplify $45 + 17 - 6$.

4. Round 465,902 to the nearest ten thousand.

5

Practice

5. Jamie and Quinn were at the batting cages. With each turn the pitching machine pitches 20 balls. Jamie hit 12 pitches and Quinn hit 14 pitches. Write a proportion for each baseball player in two ways, (a) using fractions and (b) using colons.

For each proportion, find the equivalent rate.

6. $\dfrac{46 \text{ miles}}{3 \text{ gallons}} = \dfrac{? \text{ miles}}{6 \text{ gallons}}$

7. $\dfrac{12 \text{ trees}}{5 \text{ acres}} = \dfrac{36 \text{ trees}}{? \text{ acres}}$

8. $\dfrac{24 \text{ ounces}}{8 \text{ gallons}} = \dfrac{6 \text{ ounces}}{? \text{ gallons}}$

Determine the unknown quantity.

9. $8 : 20 :: \ ? \ : 5$

10. $9 : 18 :: 4 : \ ?$

11. $6246 : 6 :: 2082 : \ ?$

Name _____ Date _____

Reflect & Review

1. Devon loves to cycle. On Monday she rode 4.75 kilometers, on Tuesday she rode 3.8 kilometers, on Thursday she rode 6.2 kilometers and on Friday she rode 8.3 kilometers. How many kilometers did she ride in all?

2. Six oranges cost $3.99. How much does one orange cost? Round your answer to the nearest cent.

3. Simplify: $(15)(6) - 8 \div 2 + 2 - 14$.

4. Find the quotient: $\dfrac{12}{25} \div \dfrac{6}{15}$.

5. Convert 467 centimeters to meters.

Practice

Complete each statement to write the rate as a unit rate.

6. $\dfrac{\$54}{3 \text{ hours}} = \dfrac{\$ (54 \div)}{(3 \div 3) \text{ hours}} = \dfrac{\$}{1 \text{ hour}}$

7. $\dfrac{320 \text{ min}}{20 \text{ days}} = \dfrac{(320 \div) \text{ min}}{(20 \div) \text{ days}} = \dfrac{\text{min}}{1 \text{ day}}$

8. $\dfrac{72 \text{ flowers}}{8 \text{ vases}} = \dfrac{(72 \div) \text{ flowers}}{(8 \div) \text{ vases}} = \dfrac{\text{flowers}}{1 \text{ vase}}$

9. $\dfrac{500 \text{ apples}}{25 \text{ trees}} = \dfrac{(500 \div) \text{ apples}}{(25 \div) \text{ trees}} = \dfrac{\text{apples}}{1 \text{ tree}}$

10. $\dfrac{418 \text{ books}}{22 \text{ shelves}} = \dfrac{(418 \div) \text{ books}}{(22 \div) \text{ shelves}} = \dfrac{\text{books}}{1 \text{ shelf}}$

11. $\dfrac{700 \text{ pens}}{20 \text{ boxes}} = \dfrac{(700 \div) \text{ pens}}{(20 \div) \text{ boxes}} = \dfrac{\text{pens}}{1 \text{ box}}$

Write the rate as a unit rate.

12. $\dfrac{72 \text{ flowers}}{8 \text{ vases}}$

13. $\dfrac{4000 \text{ chocolate chips}}{250 \text{ cookies}}$

Name _____ Date _____

© 2005 Carnegie Learning, Inc.

Reflect & Review

1. Yanni and Freeda bought 104 beads at a craft store. One-fourth of the beads are clear glass, one-half of the beads are solid-colored glass, and one-fourth of the beads are multi-colored glass. How many of each type of bead do they have?

2. At the state fair, Paula wanted to buy some homemade strawberry jelly. After looking around, she decided she wanted either Sally's Strawberry Jelly (16 ounces for $3.20) or Josh's Jelly (24 ounces for $5.28). Which person should Paula buy from to get the most for her money? Justify your answer.

3. Find the LCM of 6 and 16.

4. Show that the proportion $\frac{8}{9} = \frac{40}{45}$ is true.

Practice

Solve each proportion. Be sure to show all work.

5. $\frac{35 \text{ staples}}{7 \text{ walls}} = \frac{x \text{ staples}}{3 \text{ walls}}$

6. $\frac{124 \text{ computers}}{4 \text{ computer labs}} = \frac{620 \text{ computers}}{x \text{ computer labs}}$

5. $\frac{8 \text{ acres}}{\$24,000} = \frac{100 \text{ acres}}{\$ x}$

6. $\frac{\$5.52}{24 \text{ ounces}} = \frac{\$ x}{32 \text{ ounces}}$

5. $\frac{45 \text{ yards}}{16 \text{ carries}} = \frac{x \text{ yards}}{4 \text{ carries}}$

6. $\frac{736 \text{ grapes}}{8 \text{ vines}} = \frac{92 \text{ grapes}}{x \text{ vines}}$

11. If thirty-two cans will fit into four boxes, how many boxes will it take to pack 104 cans?

Name _____ Date _____

1. Josh and Zandra are planning a trip to an amusement park for their class. The tickets are $35.95 each and meals and snacks will cost $38 each.The school will provide transportation. There are 24 students in the class. What is the total cost for each student to go on this trip? What is the cost for the entire class?

2. Zainab has just been promoted to assistant manager. She will receive a raise that is $\frac{3}{20}$ of her original salary. If her salary is $2000 a month, what will it be after her promotion?

3. Find the product: $\frac{36}{100} \cdot \frac{75}{24}$.

4. Solve the proportion: $\frac{5}{9} \cdot \frac{20}{?}$.

5. Order the numbers from least to greatest: 0.65, $\frac{4}{7}$, 0.15, $\frac{8}{9}$, 0.1, 0.7.

Write each percent as a fraction and a decimal.

6. 4%

7. 55%

8. 80%

Write each decimal as a fraction and a percent.

9. 0.25

10. 0.3

11. 0.65

Write each fraction as a decimal and a percent.

12. $\frac{3}{5}$

13. $\frac{3}{8}$

14. $\frac{3}{4}$

Skills Practice

Name _____ Date _____

Reflect & Review

1. There are 3545 students enrolled at a local high school. Two-fifths of the students have a driver's license. How many of the students have a driver's license?

2. There are 52 playing cards in a deck. There are thirteen cards in each of the four suits. What is the ratio of the number of cards in two of the suits to the number of cards in a deck?

3. Find the least common multiple of 6 and 8.

4. Write the prime factorization of the number 54.

5. Use mental math to simplify: 14 x 22 − 100.

Practice

Find the percent of the number.

6. 1% of 380

7. 10% of 430

8. 100% of 600

Use a benchmark percent to find each percent. Show your work.

9. 25% of 200

10. 38% of 72

11. 20% of 98

12. 60% of 140

13. 72% of 300

14. 13% of 145

15. 9% of 180

16. 42% of 60

17. 99% of 550

Skills Practice

Name _____ Date _____

1. The streets running east and west in Norman, Oklahoma are named in order as multiples of twelve. If I start on 12th street and need to go south to get to 108th street how many east-west streets would I pass?

2. Lexi wants to buy a video camera. She has saved $150. At her babysitting job, she makes $10 per week. The video camera that Lexi wants costs $335. How long will it take her to save up enough money to buy the video camera?

3. Use a benchmark percent to find 30% of 150.

4. Find the greatest common factor of 16 and 28.

5. Use mental math to find the difference: 358 – 221.

Practice

Write and solve a proportion to find the percent of the number. Show all of work.p

6. 30% of 60

7. 18% of 84

8. 8% of 1200

9. 120% of 75

10. 49% of 58

11. 25% of 367

12. 15% of 240

13. 75% of 654

14. 145% of 2000

6

Skills Practice

Name _____   Date _____

1. Candace is looking for a new apartment. She has budgeted one-fourth of her paycheck each month to spend on rent. Each month she earns $2450. How much can she spend on an apartment and stay within her budget?

2. You are buying a guitar for $400. The sales tax in your state is 5%. How much sales tax will you be charged?

3. True or False: An odd number multiplied by an odd number is always odd.

4. Find the product: 0.36 x 150.   5. Use mental math to find the quotient: 565 ÷ 5.

6

Practice

Find the original price if the sale price given is 75% of the original price.

6. Sale price: $60   7. Sale price: $150   8. Sale price: $225

Find the markup price if the original price given is 90% of the markup price.

9. Original price: $36   10. Original price: $108   11. Original price: $315

Skills Practice

Name _____   Date _____

Reflect & Review

1. Gil is 47 years old. He has spent two-fifths of his life living in Europe. How many years has he spent in Europe?

2. You are in charge of fundraising for your class trip to Washington, D.C. The total price of the trip is $32,000 for your class. The fundraiser you have chosen gives you 40% of all sales. How much does your class have to sell to earn $32,000 for the trip?

3. Simplify: $12 - [8 + 4 \times (-6)] + 3$.

4. Find the least common multiple of 8, 12, and 18.

5. Is the number 38 prime or composite? Justify your answer.

Practice

Use a proportion to find the percent.

6. What percent of 50 is 20?

7. 15 is what percent of 60?

8. 65 is what percent of 520?

9. What percent of 120 is 6?

10. What percent of 80 is 70?

11. 28 is what percent of 320?

Find the amount of simple interest earned for each deposit.

12. Principal: $500
Interest Rate: 4%
Number of Years: 20

13. Principal: $450
Interest Rate: 3%
Number of Years: 15

14. Principal: $1000
Interest Rate: 3%
Number of Years: 25

Skills Practice

Name _____ Date _____

Reflect & Review

1. Donnie is a sales representative for a chemical company. He makes 25% commission on all sales. During the month of May, he sold $5600 in chemicals to businesses. How much money did he make on commission?

2. Is 321 divisible by 3? Justify your answer.

3. Round 567.3489 to the nearest thousandth.

4. Find the product: 65.38×12.3.

5. Find the quotient: $785 \div 15$.

6

Practice

Find the percent increase.

6. Original price: $45
Current price: $53.10

7. Original price: $120
Current price: $129.60

8. Original price: $124,600
Current price: $187,500

9. Original price: $65,000
Current price: $86,450

Find the percent decrease.

10. Original price: $800
Sale price: $592

11. Original price: $1200
Sale price: $1008

12. Original price: $275
Sale price: $170.50

13. Original price: $80
Sale price: $46.40

Skills Practice

Name _____ Date _____

Reflect & Review

1. Henry knows that he will receive $\frac{1}{8}$ of an inheritance. What percent of the inheritance will he receive?

2. Jake spent $1\frac{3}{4}$ hours on his homework, $\frac{1}{2}$ hours eating and $1\frac{1}{4}$ hours playing video games. If Jake got home from school at 4:30 P.M., what time did he finish all three tasks?

3. Perform the indicated operations: $\frac{7}{8} + \frac{6}{4} - \frac{1}{2}$.   4. Find the sum: 45.38 + 21.742.

5. List all of the factors of 30.

Practice

Write each gain or loss as an integer.

6. gain of 10 yards   7. a loss of 4 yards   8. gain of 18 yards

Use the symbol > for greater than and the symbol < for less than.

9. −5   −8   10. −3   0   11. 5   −5

Answer the following questions.

12. The temperature at 9:00 A.M. was 40°. At 2:00 P.M., it was −10°. What was the change in temperature?

13. Sam's savings account had $120 in it at the beginning of the month. She withdrew $50. Then she deposited $80. How much money does she have in her account now?

14. You began your hike at 30 ft below sea level. You are now at 200 ft. How far have you hiked?

Name _____ Date _____

1. Over a four-month period, a company makes a profit of $750 during the first month, a loss of $175 during the second month, a loss of $10 during the third month, and a profit of $900 during the fourth month. Write the amount of money made each month as an integer.

2. Nichole, Ann and Dawn want to drive to an amusement park. The park is 325 miles from where they live. If they drive an average of 65 miles per hour, how long will it take them to drive to the park?

3. Solve the proportion: $\dfrac{15}{63} = \dfrac{5}{x}$.

4. Convert 3245 milligrams to grams.

5. Determine whether the fractions $\dfrac{24}{36}$ and $\dfrac{6}{9}$ are equivalent. Justify your answer.

7

Practice

Find each sum.

6. $5 + (-12)$

7. $145 + (-100)$

8. $-19 + (-37)$

9. $-13 + 9$

10. $68 + (-42)$

11. $-13 + (-19)$

12. $-14 + 6 + (-3)$

13. $34 + (-6) + (-22)$

14. $-12 + (-8) + (-21)$

15. $60 + 44 + (-133)$

16. $-1 + 6 + (-7) + 3$

17. $315 + (-21) + (-315) + 45$

Name _____ Date _____

Reflect & Review

1. Olan answered 75% of the problems correctly on his math test. If there were 64 problems on the test, how many problems did he answer correctly?

2. There are 12 students on the school improvement team. For lunch, they ordered 5 pizzas. They are working in groups of 3. How should the pizza be split evenly between the groups?

3. Write the temperature 15 degrees below zero as an integer.

4. Find the product: 5.2×8.

5. Find the difference: $\dfrac{3}{5} - \dfrac{9}{4}$.

Practice

Find each difference. Then write a sentence that describes the movement on the number line that you could use to solve the problem.

6. $7 - (-6)$

7. $-5 - (-13)$

8. $22 - (-6) - 13$

Find each difference.

9. $188 - (-42)$

10. $-304 - 22$

11. $83 - 15$

12. $-173 - 47$

13. $31 - (-25) + 18 - 3$

14. $-48 - 21 + 10 - (-3)$

Skills Practice

Name _____ Date _____

Reflect & Review

1. Find the area of the figure at the right.

7 in.

14 in.

8 in.

2 in.

2. Cheryl is trying to estimate how much money she has in her checking account. Yesterday, she had $322 in her account. Since then she has purchased items with her check card and paid a bill by check. Estimate to the nearest dollar how much money Cheryl has in her checking account.

Purchased items: $32.44 and $71.38   Bill: $15.64

3. Perform the indicated operations: $6 + 9 - 16$.   **4.** List all factors of 54.

5. What is the place value of 9 in the number 43,781.029?

Practice

Find each product or quotient.

6. $8 \times (-7)$

7. $-15 \times (-2)$

8. -9×14

9. $-17 \ (-3)$

10. $-25 \div 5$

11. $81 \div (-9)$

12. $-121 \div (-11)$

13. -22×4

14. $-36 \div (-3)$

15. $625 \div (-25)$

16. -8×-12

17. $-45 \div (-9)$

Name _____ Date _____

Reflect & Review

1. You need four pieces of wood with the following lengths for a project: $3\frac{1}{8}$ feet, $5\frac{1}{2}$ feet, $2\frac{3}{4}$ feet, and 4 feet. How many feet of wood do you need?

2. At 7:00 A.M. the temperature was 38°F. A temperature reading taken at 5:00 P.M. indicated that the temperature was –5°F. Find the difference in the temperatures.

3. Use mental math to find the sum: 5600 + 210 + 45.

4. Find the product: $4\frac{1}{8} \times 2\frac{2}{11}$.

5. Order the following numbers from least to greatest: 1.12, $\frac{5}{4}$, 0.8, 1.3, $1\frac{1}{12}$.

Practice

Find each absolute value.

6. $|9 - 16|$

7. $|25 - 12|$

8. $|3 - (-11)|$

9. $|5 \times (-7)|$

10. $|9 - (-14) - 32|$

11. $|1 - 8 + (-3)|$

Complete each statement so that it is true.

12. $14 + \underline{\hspace{1cm}} = 0$

13. $4 \times \underline{\hspace{1cm}} = 1$

14. $\frac{3}{4} \times \underline{\hspace{1cm}} = 1$

7

Skills Practice

Name _____ Date _____

Reflect & Review

1. Gunner is at the grocery store buying cereal. A 12-ounce box costs $2.52 and a 16-ounce box costs $3.04. Which box is the better buy?

2. Jennifer has 20% of the problems on her achievement test completed. If there are 400 problems on the test, how many does she have left?

3. Write $\frac{46}{5}$ as a mixed number.

4. Find the quotient: 45.39 ÷ 0.3.

5. Is 528 divisible by 3? Justify your answer.

Practice

Write each number in expanded form using powers of ten.

6. 45.67

7. 123.8

8. 0.25

9. 9.17

Find each product or quotient.

10. 34.19 x 100

11. 15.227 x 10

12. 28.05 ÷ 10

13. 548.2 ÷ 100

14. 4902 x 0.01

15. 263.99 ÷ 0.001

Name _____ Date _____

1. Ray bought a set of golf clubs and accessories. He paid $330 for a set of clubs, a bag, and a golf towel. If the tax on the items is 9% of the original price, how much will it cost him to buy the clubs and accessories?

2. You are stacking five books with the following thicknesses: $2\frac{1}{8}$ inches, $4\frac{2}{5}$ inches, $1\frac{3}{4}$ inches, 3 inches, and $2\frac{3}{10}$ inches. How tall is the stack?

3. Use mental math to find the sum: 4220 + 8361.

4. Find the sum: 1.28 + 17.3 + 22.654.

5. Find all of the prime numbers between 20 and 40.

Write each number as a power with a negative exponent. Then find the value of the power.

6. $\frac{1}{7^2}$

7. $\frac{1}{4^3}$

8. $\frac{1}{10^4}$

Write each number using scientific notation.

9. 0.000023

10. 0.00763

11. 0.0001948

Write each number as a numeral.

12. 8.439×10^{-6}

13. 3.582×10^{-8}

14. 5.629×10^{-2}

Name _____ Date _____

1. A bakery sells loaves of bread for $2.35 each. On a given day, the bakery sells 210 loaves of bread. How much money do they make from the sale of the loaves of bread?

2. You counted the stamps in your collection and found that you have 42 stamps from countries other than the United States. If you have 56 more stamps from the United States than from other countries, how many stamps do you have altogether?

3. Use mental math to find the difference: 6400 + 1300.

4. Perform the indicated operations: $6 - (10 - 13)$.   5. Find all prime numbers between 20 and 40.

8

Practice

A town has two card shops, Perfect Cards and the Card Stop. On a given day, the shops together sold a total of 355 cards. Perfect Cards sold 29 more cards than the Card Stop.

6. Draw a diagram that represents this situation.

7. How many cards did each shop sell?

8. Let p represent the number of cards sold by Perfect Cards and let c represent the number of cards sold by the Card Stop. Use the variables to write an equation that represents the total number of cards sold.

On your bookshelf, you have a total of 61 books. The number of paperback books that you have is 4 more than two times the number of hardcover books you have.

9. Draw a diagram that represents this situation.

10. How many of each kind of book do you have?

Name _____ Date _____

Reflect & Review

1. A water park sells season passes for $61.50 including tax. Your mom wants to buy passes for the whole family, 6 people. How much would she have to pay for the season passes?

2. Robin is 3 years older than Brent. Sally is 4 years younger than Brent. Robin is 12 years old. What are the ages of Brent and Sally?

3. Simplify: $8 \times 9 - 15 \div 3 + 8 - 32$.

4. Find the product: $6 \times (-9)$.

5. Use mental math to find the difference: $1450 - 725$.

Practice

6. A copy machine makes 35 copies per minute. Let m represent the number of minutes the copier runs. Write an expression that represents the total number of copies made.

7. Kate can make a dozen cookies out of each ready-bake cookie roll. Let r represent each ready-bake cookie roll. Write an expression that represents the total number of cookies she can make.

8. Fifteen baseballs can fit into each display case. Let c represent the number of display cases. Write an expression that represents the total number of baseballs in cases.

9. Kendal earns $15 each night he works at a Mexican restaurant and $5 per hour in tips. Let h represent the number of hours he works. Write an expression that represents the total amount of earnings.

Evaluate each expression for the given values.

10. $-2y$ when $y = 0$, 6, and -3.

11. $-8x + 7$ when $x = -1$, 2, and 5.

12. $5.2r + 1.2$ when $r = -4$, 0, and 1.5.

13. $\frac{1}{2}t + \frac{3}{4}$ when $t = -8$, $\frac{1}{2}$, and $\frac{2}{3}$

Name _____ Date _____

1. Find the perimeter of a square with side length of $3\frac{1}{8}$ centimeters.

2. A local real estate agent earns 3% of the sale price of a house. If a house sells for $150,000, how much would he earn?

3. Evaluate $5 - 8t$ when $t = -2$ and 5.

4. Find the product: $\frac{5}{6} \times \frac{15}{8} \times \frac{24}{25}$.

5. True or False: The product of two odd integers is an even integer. Justify your answer.

Practice

Solve each equation. Show your work.

6. $4x = 24$

7. $r + 7 = 8$

8. $12x = 36$

9. $m - 34 = 58$

10. $\frac{2}{3}b = \frac{4}{9}$

11. $1.6g = 2.4$

12. $5.2t = -1.3$

13. $\frac{3}{5}b = \frac{18}{25}$

14. $87 + p = 167$

Name _____ Date _____

Reflect & Review

1. Belinda works at the Pizza Galore where she earns $6 per hour. She wants to buy a CD player for her car that costs $358. How many hours does she need to work to earn enough money to buy the CD player?

2. Pablo wants to arrange his coin collection in a shadow box. He has 64 coins and wants the arrangement to be rectangular. Describe the ways in which Pablo can arrange his coins.

3. Solve the proportion: $\frac{5}{8} = \frac{x}{24}$.

4. Use mental math to find the product: 3200 x 40.

5. Find the quotient: 453.2 ÷ 0.04.

8

Practice

Solve each equation. Show your work.

6. $4t - 8 = 12$

7. $5 - 3v = -10$

8. $9 = 6y + 21$

9. $-50t + 10 = 35$

10. $17 = 9c - 19$

11. $4r + 22 = -102$

12. $-\frac{1}{3}t + \frac{2}{9} = \frac{7}{9}$

13. $2 = \frac{3}{2}p - 10$

14. $145 - 18n = -125$

Name _____   Date _____

Reflect & Review

1. Barbara works for a car dealership near her house. She earns 15% commission on all sales. If she sells four cars totaling $62,539, what are her total earnings in commission?

2. A rectangular pool measures 20 feet by 12 feet. What is the area of the pool?

3. Perform the indicated operations: $\dfrac{2}{5} = \dfrac{3}{2} - \dfrac{13}{10}$.

4. Write $6\dfrac{4}{5}$ as a decimal.

5. Find all of the prime numbers between 50 and 60.

8

Practice

Plot each point on the coordinate plane at the right.

6. A(4, 3)

7. B(2.5, 7)

8. C(0, 4)

9. D(9, 0)

10. $E\left(2\dfrac{3}{4}, 5\dfrac{1}{2}\right)$

11. F(1, 7)

12. G(7, 2)

13. H(3, 5.5)

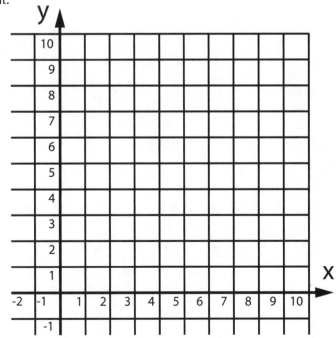

© 2005 Carnegie Learning, Inc.

Skills Practice

Name _____ Date _____

Reflect & Review

1. Jade has 42 candy bars left to sell for a fundraiser. The candy bars are $1.50 each. She has $165 to turn in for candy bars sold. After she sells the rest of the candy bars, how much money will she turn in?

2. There are sixteen songs on a CD. Each song is about 4 minutes and 30 seconds long. How long will it take to listen to the entire CD?

3. Find the quotient: $2.19 \div 0.6$

4. Convert 23,760 feet to miles.

Practice

Complete each table.

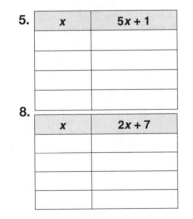

5.

x	5x + 1

6.

x	6x + 2

7.

x	6x + 2

8.

x	2x + 7

9.

x	6x + 1

10.

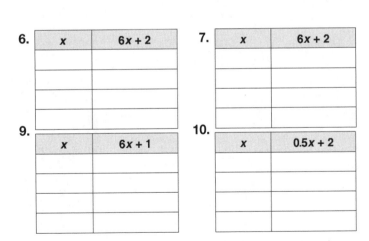

x	0.5x + 2

11. Create a graph from the table in Question 6.

12. Create a graph from the table in Question 10.

Skills Practice

Name _____ Date _____

1. You and five friends go to the movie theater. The theater gives a 10% discount on a ticket with a student ID. A ticket for the matinee costs $6. If you and your friends all have student IDs, how much will it cost you to go to the matinee?

2. Mike has completed 20 out of 30 passes at football practice so far. If he throws a total of 45 passes, how many passes do you expect him to complete?

3. Decide where to place the parentheses so that the answer is correct using the order of operations.
   $4 \times 8 + 15 - 8 \div 3 = 20$

4. Write $15 \frac{4}{9}$ as a mixed number.

5. Write the prime factorization of the number 24.

Practice

Use the diagram at the right to answer the following questions.

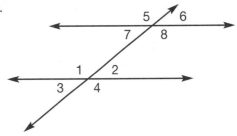

6. Name all of the pairs of vertical angles.

7. Name all of the pairs of alternate interior angles.

8. Name all of the pairs of supplementary angles.

9. Name all of the pairs of corresponding angles.

10. If $m\angle 2 = 35°$, find $m\angle 4$, $m\angle 8$, $m\angle 3$, and $m\angle 7$.

11. If $m\angle 1 = 115°$, find $m\angle 2$, $m\angle 5$, and $m\angle 6$.

Skills Practice

Name _____ Date _____

Reflect & Review

1. Julianna is buying hotdogs and buns for the cookout. Hotdogs come in packages of ten and buns come in packages of eight. How many packages of hotdogs and buns should she buy so that she doesn't have any dogs or buns left over?

2. Herb has $40. He buys 4 pounds of grapes for $2.45 per pound. How much money does he have left?

3. Use mental math to find the sum: 6522 + 471.

4. Find the product: 1.45 x 32.8.

Practice

Classify each triangle by its sides and angles.

5.

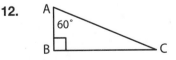

6.

7.

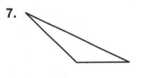

Draw a triangle with the given characteristics. If it is not possible, explain why.

8. An isosceles right triangle

9. A scalene acute triangle

10. An obtuse equilateral triangle

11. An obtuse scalene triangle

Find the missing angle measure.

12.

A
60°
B C

13.

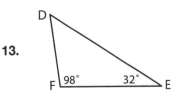

Name _____ Date _____

Reflect & Review

1. Chris is assigning starting times to 48 golfers. First he put thems in groups of four. Now he needs to tell each group what time to start. The first group will begin at 7:30 A.M. and the last group needs to begin at 10:30 A.M. How many groups are there? If there is an equal number of minutes between each starting time, how many minutes are there between one starting time and the next starting time?

2. The photo gallery wants to print a flyer to advertise its portrait studio. Mr. Gray wants to place 8 pictures on the page in rows so that each row has the same number of pictures. You have the ability to shrink and enlarge the pictures to fit on the flyer. What are the different arrangements for the pictures?

9

3. List the next four prime numbers after 37.

4. Find the sum: $3\frac{5}{8} + 2\frac{1}{3}$.

Practice

Write as many names as you can for each quadrilateral.

5.
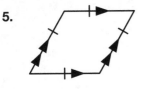

6.

7.
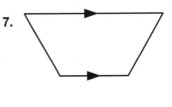

Classify the polygon by its sides.

8.

9.

10.

Find the measure of the missing angle of each polygon.

11.
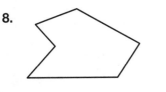

12.
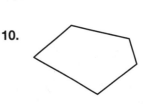

Name _____   Date _____

Reflect & Review

1. You are building a raised garden bed that is 6 feet long and 3 feet wide. What is the perimeter of the raised garden bed?

2. Your friend is making pillows to earn money this summer. One yard of material costs $1.34. She uses $3\frac{1}{2}$ yards to make each pillow. How much does the material for one pillow cost? She sells the pillows for $10. How much does she make on each pillow after subtracting the cost of material?

3. Find the quotient: $0.25 \div 5$.

4. Perform the indicated operations: $\frac{4}{7} \times \frac{9}{8} \div \frac{18}{35}$.

9

Practice

The figures shown are similar. Name the corresponding angles and corresponding sides of each pair of figures.

5.

6.

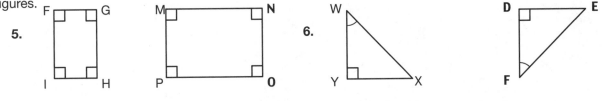

Find the scale factor used to produce the new figure.

6. Rectangle A is enlarged to make rectangle B.   **7.** Rectangle C is reduced to make rectangle D.

10. Triangle *BAT* is similar to triangle *SIP*. Find the missing side lengths.

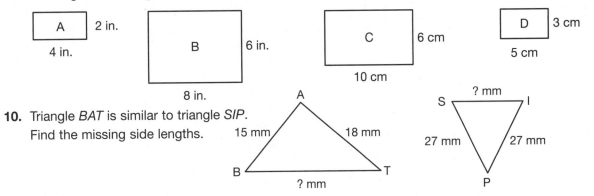

Skills Practice

Name _____ Date _____

Reflect & Review

1. You are in charge of restocking the paper cups in the concession stand at the football field. At Discount Paper, 500 cups cost $220, and at Paper Supply, 275 cups cost $115.50. Which store has better pricing for cups? Justify your answer.

2. An 8-inch by 10-inch picture frame is shown at the right. A two-inch mat has been placed inside the frame. Find the area of the mat.

3. Find the product: 5.78×0.2.

4. Find the greatest common factor of 36 and 48.

5. Find the sum: $7.03 + 9 + 11.28$.

9

Practice

Use a proportion and similar triangles to find the missing length. Show your work.

6.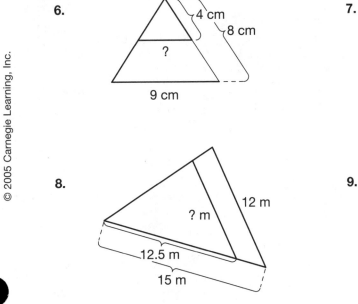

7.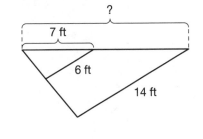

8.

9.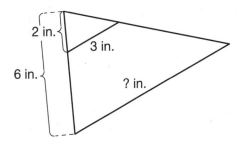

© 2005 Carnegie Learning, Inc.

Name _____ Date _____

1. Two-fifths of the senior class voted that "Spirit Week" be held in October. One-fifth of the senior class voted that it be held in September. If there are 455 students in the senior class, how many students did not vote that "Spirit Week" be held in September or October?

2. Jake traveled 469 miles to his grandmother's house. If he drove at an average speed of 67 miles per hour, how many hours did he drive?

3. Find the difference: $\frac{3}{4} - \frac{8}{11}$.

4. Solve the proportion: $\frac{21}{15} = \frac{x}{5}$.

5. Write $\frac{78}{1}$ as a mixed number.

Practice

Sketch the following figures on the grid below.

6. A rectangle that is similar to rectangle ABCD with a scale factor of 3

7. A rectangle that is congruent to rectangle ABCD

8. A rectangle that is similar to rectangle ABCD with scale factor of 0.25

9. A triangle that is congruent to triangle STR

10. A triangle that is similar to triangle STR with scale factor of 2

11. A triangle that is similar to triangle STR with scale factor of 0.5

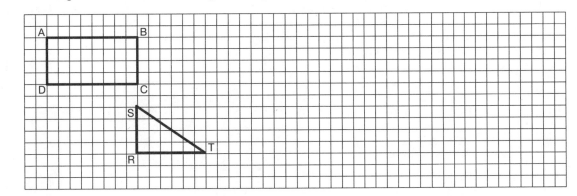

Name _____   Date _____

© 2005 Carnegie Learning, Inc.

Reflect & Review

1. Josh's flight leaves the airport at 8 A.M. The flight lasts 2 hours. He has to wait 2 hours before leaving on a flight that will get him to his destination. This flight lasts 3 hours. What time does he arrive at his destination?

2. Deana has a bottle of 300 vitamins. If she takes one a day, how many weeks will the vitamins last?

3. Find the area of a rectangle whose length is 4.5 meters and whose width is 2.7 meters.

4. Perform the indication operations: $\frac{32}{8} \cdot \frac{6}{24} \div \frac{27}{18}$.   **5.** List all of the prime numbers between 50 and 60.

10

Practice

Find the possible lengths and widths of rectangles with the given area. Then find the perimeters of these rectangles.

6. Area: 18 square units

Length	Width	Perimeter

7. Area: 24 square units

Length	Width	Perimeter

8. Area: 12 square units

Length	Width	Perimeter

9. Area: 42 square units

Length	Width	Perimeter

Find the possible lengths and widths of rectangles with the given perimeter. Then find the areas of these rectangles.

10. Perimeter: 18 units

Length	Width	Area

11. Perimeter: 10 units

Length	Width	Area

Name _____ Date _____

Reflect & Review

1. Helen can transfer 24 pictures from a memory card to a CD in 2 minutes. At this rate, how many pictures can she transfer in one hour? Justify your answer.

2. Your teacher has decided to make a memory quilt for your class. Each student will design one square. There are 32 students in your class. What are the different ways that the squares can be arranged in rows and columns? Which dimension will your teacher be most likely to use and why?

10

3. Solve the equation 3x + 8 = −16.

4. Write the prime factorization of the number 48.

5. Order the numbers from least to greatest: $2.3, \ -1.5, \ \dfrac{9}{4}, \ 2.8, \ -2, \ -\dfrac{7}{3}, \ 1, \ -1$

Practice

Find the missing information for each circle. Write your answers in terms of π when necessary.

6. Radius: 4 in.
   Diameter:
   Circumference:
   Area:

7. Radius:
   Diameter: 10 m
   Circumference:
   Area:

8. Radius:
   Diameter:
   Circumference: 24 π in.
   Area:

Determine which figure has the greater area. Justify your answer.

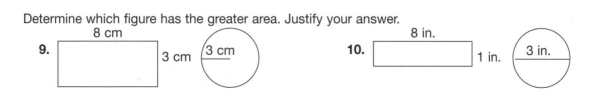

9. 8 cm / 3 cm / 3 cm

10. 8 in. / 1 in. / 3 in.

Name _____ Date _____

1. You are attending a conference for your company. The round trip is 328 miles and your company will pay you $0.42 per mile for using your own car. How much will you be paid for the round trip?

2. Find the maximum area of a rectangle that has perimeter of 16 feet.

3. Use mental math to find the sum: 93 + 48.

4. Find the greatest common factor of 8 and 12.

5. Find the quotient: 136.91 ÷ 2.1.

10

Find the area of each figure.

6.

8 in.

12 in.

7.

10 mm

5 mm

16 mm

8.

9 ft

4 ft

← 5.5 ft →

9.

20 in.

7 in.

10.

3 m

5 m

© 2005 Carnegie Learning, Inc.

Name _____ Date _____

1. A patio is built in the shape of a trapezoid as shown. Find the area of the patio.

15 ft

8 ft

6 ft

2. What is the area of a 14-inch by 14-inch pizza box?

3. Simplify: $\dfrac{264}{312}$.

4. 54 is what percent of 86? Round your answer to the nearest tenth.

5. Name the ordered pair whose point is 6 units to the right of the y-axis and 2 units above the x-axis.

10

Write the square root of each perfect square.

6. $\sqrt{81}$

7. $\sqrt{225}$

8. $\sqrt{64}$

Complete the statement with two integers so that the perfect squares are the perfect squares closest to the number.

9. $\_^2 < 19 < \_^2$

10. $\_^2 < 93 < \_^2$

11. $\_^2 < 40 < \_^2$

Estimate the square root to the nearest tenth.

12. $\sqrt{14}$

13. $\sqrt{56}$

14. $\sqrt{19}$

15. $\sqrt{35}$

16. $\sqrt{102}$

17. $\sqrt{73}$

Name _____ Date _____

1. Josh wants to put a fence around his rectangular basketball court. The court is 51.5 feet long and 38.75 feet wide. How many feet of fencing will Josh need?

2. If the fencing Josh chose in Question 1 costs $5.38 per foot, how much would it cost to fence the basketball court?

3. Use mental math to subtract: 941 − 240.

4. Simplify: $\dfrac{54}{36} \bullet \dfrac{72}{66}$.

5. Matt played 72 baseball games last summer. If his team won 58 games, what was percent of the games did they win? Round your answer to the nearest whole percent.

Use the Pythagorean Theorem to find the missing side length.

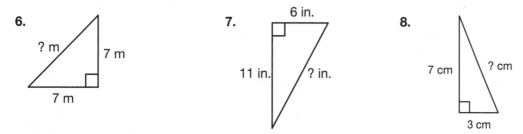

6.   ? m   7 m
      7 m

7.   6 in.
      11 in.   ? in.

8.   7 cm   ? cm
      3 cm

Plot the following points in a coordinate plane and use the Pythagorean Theorem to find the length of the hypotenuse.

9. *A*(0, 1), *B*(0, 7), *C*(8, 1)

10. *E*(1, 4), *F*(1, 0), *G*(8, 4)

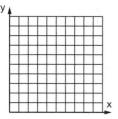

Name _____   Date _____

Reflect & Review

1. Paul and Moriah are trying to find the shortest route to their favorite restaurant. They have narrowed their search down to two routes which form a right triangle. The legs of the triangle are 8*m* and 10*m*. Would it be a shorter distance traveling the legs of the triangle or the hypotenuse? Justify your answer.

2. Elise purchased her house for $75,000. Today it is worth $138,000. Find the percent increase in the value of her house.

3. Simplify: $18 - 33 \ 2 + 48 \div 6 + 20$.

4. Evaluate $6r^2 - 9r + 7$ when $r = -2$.

5. Solve the equation: $4x - 10 = 22$.

Practice

Determine whether the triangle is a right triangle.

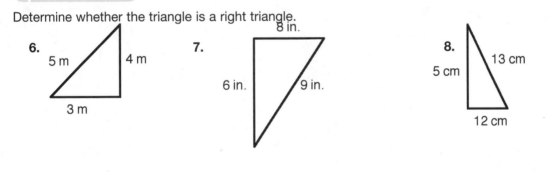

6. 5 m   4 m   3 m

7. 8 in.   6 in.   9 in.

8. 5 cm   13 cm   12 cm

9. Eric is designing a geometric statue for an arts festival. The base of the statue is a right triangle. If the lengths of the legs are 13 inches and 84 inches, how long is the hypotenuse?

Name _____   Date _____

Reflect & Review

1. Kelly has hand-written a biology report that is 2000 words long. She can type about 47 words per minute. How long will it take her to type the report? Round your answer to the nearest minute

   Number of minutes = 2000 ÷ 47 = 43

2. Solve the equation: $18 = 14 - \dfrac{1}{6}x$.

3. Simplify the expression: $\dfrac{6 + 8}{20}$.

4. You have completed 24 of 50 homework problems. Write the ratio that represents the portion of problems you have completed.

11

Practice

There are 12 socks in a drawer–4 of them are white, 6 of them are blue, and 2 of them are black.

5. What is the probability that you will pull out a white sock?

6. What is the probability that you will pull out a blue sock?

7. What is the probability that you will pull out a black sock?

8. What is the probability that you will pull out a sock that is not blue?

9. What is the probability that you will pull out a sock that is not white?

10. What is the probability that you will pull out a sock that is not black?

John has 7 dimes, 9 quarters and 3 nickels in his pocket.

11. What is the probability that he will randomly pull a quarter out of his pocket?

12. What is the probability that he will randomly pull a dime out of his pocket?

13. What is the probability that he will pull a nickel out of his pocket?

Name _____ Date _____

1. You are burning 12 songs to a CD for your friend. You want to type the names of the songs on a piece of paper and put it in the CD case. You want to arrange the names in rows and columns so that all of the rows have the same number of songs and all of the columns have the same number of songs. How many different arrangements are possible? Space is not a problem— you can always choose a smaller font.

2. Find the area of the garden shown at the right. Round your answer to the nearest foot.

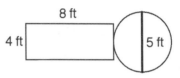

3. Sally works 5.75 hours on Mondays, Tuesdays and Thursdays. On Saturdays, she works 7.5 hours. If her earnings are $6.75 per hour, how much will she make in one week?

4. Use mental math to find the product: 300 x 120.   5. Write the next three prime numbers after 71.

You have 8 blue marbles, 9 red marbles, and 3 green marbles in a bag. You reach into the bag without looking and pull out a marble.

6. Suppose that you pull out a green marble, put it back, and pull out another marble. What is the probability that the second marble is red?

7. Suppose that you pull out a blue marble, put it back, and pull out another marble. What is the probability that the second marble is blue?

8. Suppose that you pull out a red marble, do not put it back, and pull out another marble. What is the probability that the second marble is blue?

9. Suppose that you pull out a green marble, do not put it back, and pull out another marble. What is the probability that the second marble is green?

10. What is the probability of pulling two red marbles from the bag if you pull one red marble, put it back into the bag, and then pull a second red marble?

© 2005 Carnegie Learning, Inc.

11

Name _____ Date _____

1. You have $200 saved and you are spending it at the rate of $5 per week. Write an algebraic expression that represents this situation.

2. You buy a bag of 12 guitar picks for $2.04. How much does one pick cost?

3. Perform the indicated operations: $\frac{4}{3} + \frac{7}{6} - \frac{9}{4}$.   **4.** Find the sum: 327.8 + 42.03 + 87.

5. Evaluate $7x + 5$ when $x = -3$.

11

Practice

Fir.d the mean, median, mode and range of the set of data. Round your answers to the nearest hundredth when necessary.

6. 14, 19, 8, 22, 11, 19, 4, 18, 12, 10, 21

7. 55, 24, 73, 108, 39, 46, 72, 100, 92, 32

Name _____ Date _____

1. Nelly has found a house she would like to buy. Her down payment for the house must be 20% of the sale price. If the price of the house she found was $240,000, what will her down payment be?

2. Chloe is taking round beads out of a jar. She knows that there are 15 purple beads, 18 grey beads, and 22 black beads. Without looking at what color of bead she is choosing, what is the probability that she will chose a purple bead?

3. Perform the indicated operations: $(18 - 15 \times 3) - 2(5 + 4)$.

4. Find the product: 6.2×0.4.

5. Solve the proportion: $\dfrac{6}{25} = \dfrac{18}{x}$.

Practice

6. Construct a histogram of the data in the frequency table.

Data Intervals	0.0-0.9	1.0-1.9	2.0-2.9	3.0-3.9
Tally |卌	|||			卌 ||
Frequency	5	3	1	7

7. Construct a frequency table and histogram of the data.

22, 4, 20, 11, 31, 5, 27, 7, 19, 3, 1, 15, 29, 9, 22, 35, 12, 0, 2, 25, 38

Data Intervals	0-9	10-19	20-29	30-39
Tally				
Frequency				

Name _____ Date _____

Reflect & Review

1. Ritchie challenged Shelia to a basketball contest. Ritchie said he could make 19 out of 25 three pointers and Shelia said she makes a basket 81% of the time from the three-point line. Who do you think will make the most out of 100 three pointers based on the information given? Justify your answer.

2. Your cell phone provider charges you $0.13 per minute for calls when you have used more than 1400 minutes. You are also charged a monthly fee of $29.95. Last month you used 2278 minutes. How much was last month's phone bill?

3. Perform the indicated operations: $58 - (-345) - 721 + 32$.

4. At graduation, two-thirds of the class wore sandals. Twenty-seven people graduated. How many did *not* wear sandals?

11

Practice

Use the stem-and-leaf plot to identify the mean, median, and mode(s) of the data.

5.

1	9
2	1 2 5 8
3	0 1 2 6
4	5

$1 | 0 = 10$

6.

5	3 3 4
6	0 4 8 8
7	1 1 2 6
8	0 1

$1 | 0 = 1.0$

Make a stem-and-leaf plot of the data.

7. 46, 57, 61, 11, 43, 7, 42, 16, 54, 14, 46, 0, 28, 4, 19, 49, 7, 6, 52, 10, 21, 43

8. 7.8, 5.0, 4.6, 8.5, 7.1, 6.4, 7.7, 3.8, 7.5, 5.4, 6.6, 4.0, 3.7, 9.8, 5.1, 4.9, 3.9, 5.8, 6.2, 8.5

Name _____ Date _____

1. Yolanda made golf putts from distances of 7 feet, 15 feet, 8 feet, 9.5 feet, and 11 feet from the hole. Of the putts she made, what is the average distance from the hole?

2. When contractors lay tile in a house, they order 10% extra for breakage. A job requires 150 tiles. How many tiles should the contractor order?

3. What is 15% of 75?

4. Find the product: 0.81 x 3.54.

11

Practice

Find the median, upper quartile, and lower quartile of the data.

5. 5, 18, 15, 8, 12, 10, 8, 4, 1, 10, 11, 3, 15

6. 65, 69, 52, 64, 59, 48, 44, 56, 70, 38, 40

Name _____   Date _____

Reflect & Review

1. Sandy is building a Web page for a customer. She charges a flat fee of $75 and $15.95 a month for maintenance. How much would it cost the customer to pay for one year of service?

2. If a basketball team makes 65% of its baskets from the field, how many attempts would they have to take to make 26 baskets?

3. Use mental math to find the product: $60 \times \frac{1}{2}$.

4. Simplify: $\frac{198}{270}$.

5. Perform the indicated operation: $37.8 + 42.01 - 16$

Practice

A bakery manager collects information about the bakery's sales and organizes the results in the table below. Complete the table and then construct a circle graph for the table.

6.

Bread Flavor	Number Sold	Percent of Total Sold
White	190	
Wheat	200	
Rye	50	
Pumpernickel	20	
Oatmeal	40	

Skills Practice

Name _____ Date _____

Reflect & Review

1. You are on the school track team and you throw the discus. During a warm-up at a recent practice, you throw the discus distances of 8.75 feet, 9.5 feet, and 8 feet. What is the average of these distances?

2. You want to buy a guitar that costs $328. The sales tax on the guitar is 7%. How much sales tax do you have to pay if you buy the guitar?

3. Simplify: $5 + 24 \div 3 + 4 \times 6$.

4. Find the sum: $4\frac{3}{8} + 5\frac{2}{3}$.

5. Use mental math to find the difference: $170.5 - 65.25$.

Practice

Identify the bases and the faces of each prism.

6.

7.

Identify each solid.

8.

9.

10.

Name _____ Date _____

1. A playground is being built at the new elementary school near your school. The playground will take up a rectangular area and will be 120 feet wide and 140 feet long. What will the area of the playground be?

2. Tara works at a shoe store and makes an 8% commission on each pair of shoes she sells. On a Saturday, she sells $380 worth of shoes. What is her commission?

3. Find the area of the triangle.

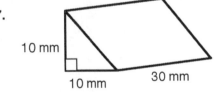

6 cm

15 cm

12

4. Find the difference: $7\dfrac{2}{3} - 4\dfrac{1}{6}$.

5. Simplify: $\dfrac{4(2) + 2(2)}{3}$

Practice

Fird the volume of the solid.

6.

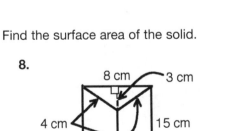

5 in.

5 in.

12 in.

7.

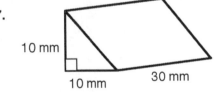

10 mm

10 mm   30 mm

Find the surface area of the solid.

8.

8 cm   3 cm

4 cm   15 cm

9.

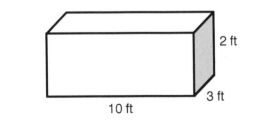

2 ft

3 ft

10 ft

Name _____ Date _____

Reflect & Review

1. A circular mural is being painted on the wall at the entrance of your school. The finished mural will have a diameter of 8 feet. What is the area of the mural? Use 3.14 for π.

2. An office supply store sells four three-ring binders for $9.52. Another store sells five three-ring binders for $11.80. Which store sells the binders for a better price?

3. Find the area of the rectangle.

8 mm

14.5 mm

12

4. Simplify: 2.4(72) + 5.

5. Find the product: 6.4 x 1.3.

Practice

Find the volume of the cylinder. Use 3.14 for π.

6.

10 m

4 m

7.

18 cm

2 cm

Find the surface area of the cylinder. Use 3.14 for π.

8.

4 in.

12 in.

9.

5 ft

3 ft

Name _____ Date _____

Reflect & Review

1. Your favorite video game is on sale for 15% off of the original price. If the video game was originally $35, how much is it now?

2. A merry-go-round has a diameter of 12 feet. What is the area of the surface of the merry-go-round? Use 3.14 for π.

3. Find the area of the rectangle.

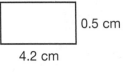
0.5 cm

4.2 cm

12

4. Simplify: $6(4^2) + 3(8)$.

Practice

5. What is the volume of a square pyramid with a base of 4 cm and a height of 6 cm? Use 3.14 for π.

6. What is the volume of a triangular pyramid with a base area of 100 square feet and a height of 15 feet? Use 3.14 for π.

7. What is the volume of a cone with a height of 15 in and a diameter of 12 in? Use 3.14 for π.

8. What is the volume of a cone with a height of 30 mm and a radius of 20 mm? Use 3.14 for π.

Name _____ Date _____

1. You want to bake 4 batches of cookies for a friend's birthday party. One batch of the recipe calls for $\frac{3}{4}$ cup of sugar and $1\frac{1}{2}$ cups of flour. How many cups of sugar and flour will you need to make the cookies?

2. You and four of your friends are going to a music concert. One ticket to the concert costs $12.95. How much will it cost for all of you to buy tickets to the concert?

3. Simplify: $\frac{2}{3}(42)(9) \cdot$

4. Simplify: $\frac{7(4) + 3(5)}{6 + 4}$.

5. Write $7\frac{5}{8}$ as an improper fraction.

6. What is the volume of a sphere with a diameter of 10 m? Use 3.14 for π.

7. What is the volume of a hemisphere with a radius of 2.5 in? Use 3.14 for π.

8. What is the surface area of a sphere with a diameter of 6 cm? Use 3.14 for π.

9. What is the surface area of a sphere with a radius of 8 ft? Use 3.14 for π.

12

Name _____ Date _____

Reflect & Review

1. Leila and two friends are driving together to a meeting. They will split the cost of the car that they rented for the trip. The total cost of the car rental is $249.30. How much will each person pay?

2. A carpenter is measuring a room so that she can install wood molding (wood strips) where the walls meet the floors. She needs strips with the following lengths: $6 \frac{1}{2}$ feet, $2 \frac{1}{4}$ feet, 8 feet, $4 \frac{3}{8}$ feet, and $5 \frac{1}{2}$ feet. How much wood will she need altogether?

3. Identify the solid.

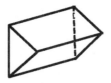

12

4. Find the quotient: $127.5 \div 0.5$.

5. Simplify: $4(62) + 5$.

Practice

Identify the solid that is formed by the net.

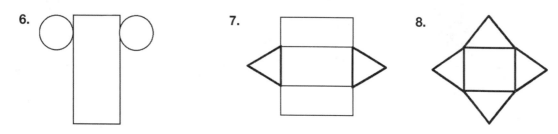

6.

7.

8.

9. Draw the six views (top, front, left side, right side, bottom, back) of the solid.

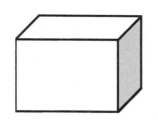

Skills Practice

Name _____ Date _____

Reflect & Review

1. Three-eighths of a senior class participated in a play. If there are 544 people in the senior class, how many people did not participate in the play?

2. You have read 138 pages of a 230-page book. What fraction of the book do you have left to read?

3. Find the sum: $-\dfrac{4}{7} = 2\dfrac{1}{2}$.

4. Solve the proportion: $\dfrac{4}{25} = \dfrac{x}{40}$.

12

Practice

Write a ratio that compares the volume of solid A to the volume of solid B. Then write a ratio that compares the surface area of sold A to the surface area of solid B.

5.

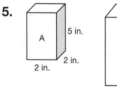
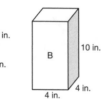

6.

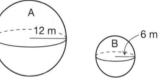

7.

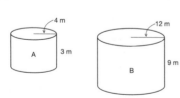

Name _____ Date _____

Reflect & Review

1. Victoria is covering a bulletin board that is $11\frac{1}{2}$ inches wide and 18 inches long with material. How much material will she need to cover this bulletin board?

2. Matt rolls two number cubes. What is the probability that both number cubes will land on a 5?

3. Find the product of 324 and 2.5.

4. Find the quotient: $\frac{3}{7} \div \frac{21}{15}$.

Practice

Decide whether the relation is a function.

5. (1, 2), (3, 4), (5, 6), (7, 8)

6. (1, 4), (2, 6), (3, 8), (1, 10), (5, 12)

For each function, identify the independent variable and the dependent variable.

7. A pizza is $8.00 and $0.50 for each additional topping.

8. The depth of the water depends on the rate of the water flow into the pool.

9. The cost of a cell phone is $0.15 per minute in addition to the $25.99 monthly charge.

Find the value of each function when $x = 4$.

10. $f(x) = 8x$

11. $f(x) = 12 - x$

12. $f(x) = x + 20$

13. What are the domain and range of the function given in the table?

x	2	4	6	8	10
y	1	3	5	7	9

Name _____ Date _____

1. Below are six quiz scores from your science class. Each quiz was worth 25 points. Find the mean, median, mode and range of the quiz scores.

   17, 20, 23, 18, 21, 24

2. A circular inflatable swimming pool has a diameter of 40 feet. Find the area of the base of the pool. Round your answer to the nearest square foot.

3. Use mental math to find the difference: 1600 − 350.

4. Find the sum: $\frac{5}{8} + \frac{2}{3} - \frac{1}{6}$.

13

Practice

Complete the input-output table for the linear function.

5.

x	f(x) = 9x
0	
1	
2	
3	

6.

x	f(x) = x + 6
10	
20	
30	
40	

7.

x	f(x) = 2x + 3
0	
1	
2	
3	

Complete the table by writing each row of numbers as an ordered pair. Then plot the points in the coordinate plane and draw a straight line through the points.

8.

x	f(x) = 3x + 1	Ordered Pairs
0	1	
1	4	
2	7	
3	10	

9.

x	f(x) = 4x − 1	Ordered Pairs
1	3	
2	7	
3	11	
4	15	

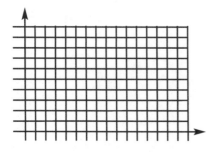

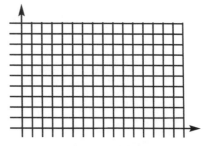

Name _____ Date _____

Reflect & Review

1. You are assembling pizzas for a fundraiser and you have assembled 6 pizzas so far. You can make 10 pizzas in one hour. Let *h* represent the number of hours you make pizzas after the first 6 pizzas. Use the variable to write an expression that represents this situation.

2. Your favorite book is on sale for 10% off of the regular price. If the book is regularly $65, how much is it on sale for?

13

3. Simplify: $\dfrac{180}{210}$.

4. Simplify: $\dfrac{4+6}{11-3}$.

Practice

Find the slope of the line given in the graph.

5.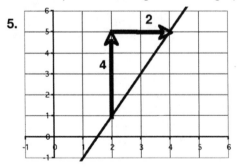

6.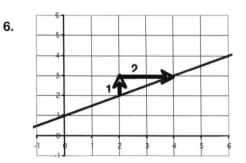

7. The graph shows the number of miles you run for different numbers of days. What is the slope of the line? Include the units in your answer.

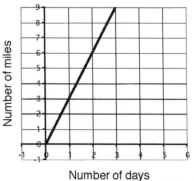

Number of days

Name _____ Date _____

Reflect & Review

1. The real estate tax on a house is about 1% of the value of the house. If a house is appraised at $193,500, how much is the real estate tax?

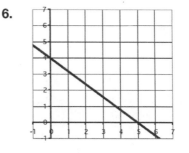

13 in.

8 in.

14 in.

2. Find the area of the trapezoid.

3. Use mental math to simplify: $1500 - 400 + 25$.   **4.** Solve the equation: $4x + 7 = 11$.

13

Practice

Find the slope and x- and y-intercepts of the linear function given by the graph.

5.

6.

Complete the ratio to find the slope of the line through the given points.

7. $(x_1, y_1) = (4, 5); (x_2, y_2) = (7, 9)$

$$\frac{(y_2 - y_1)}{(x_2 - x_1)} = \frac{\quad - \quad}{\quad - \quad} = \underline{\quad}$$

8. $(x_1, y_1) = (1, 6); (x_2, y_2) = (4, 2)$

$$\frac{(y_2 - y_1)}{(x_2 - x_1)} = \frac{\quad - \quad}{\quad - \quad} = \underline{\quad}$$

9. Find the slope and x- and y-intercepts of the linear function given by the table.

x	y
0	0
1	6
3	18
4	24

Name _____ Date _____

1. Each person in your history class has to give an oral report. Your teacher has written the names of all twenty students in your class on separate pieces of paper. She then places the names in a bag and chooses one randomly to determine who will give the first report. What is the probability that you will be chosen first?

2. What is the probability that you were chosen second if someone else was chosen first?

3. Simplify: $\dfrac{45}{144}$.

4. Find the product: 73.1 x 0.06.

13

Practice

Identify the slope and y-intercept of each line.

5. $y = 4x$ **6.** $y = -3x + 1$ **7.** $y = 6x - 5$

Find the x- and y-intercepts for the graph of the equation. Show your work.

8. $y = 7x$ **9.** $y = -5x + 5$ **10.** $y = -2x + 6$

Graph the linear equation written in slope-intercept form.

11. $y = x + 3$ **12.** $y = 0.5x + 1$

Skills Practice

Name _____ Date _____

Reflect & Review

1. Your family drives to San Diego every summer to visit your aunt. The round trip is 1274 miles. If your can travel 22 miles on one gallon of gasoline, how many gallons of gasoline will you use on the trip? Round your answer to the nearest whole gallon.

2. The height of a tree can grow up to 10 cm per year.

   a. Write an equation for the growth of the tree where x represents the number of years.

   b. Find the height of a tree after 7 years.

3. Evaluate $4x + 9$ when $x = -1$.

4. Find the difference: $9\frac{3}{8} - 5\frac{5}{8}$.

5. Find the product: 43.5×2.6.

Practice

Determine whether the two sets of data in the scatter plot have a positive relationship, a negative relationship, or no relationship.

6.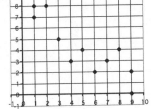

7.

8.

Draw a line of best fit for the data on the scatter plot.

9.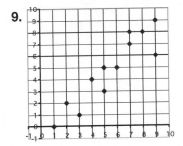

10.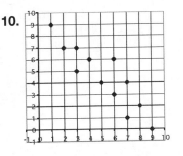

Skills Practice

Name _____ Date _____

Reflect & Review

1. The high temperatures in a city for a week were recorded as 98°F, 101°F, 93°F, 96°F, 92°F, 103°F, and 95°F. What was the average high temperature for the week? Round your answer to the nearest tenth of a degree.

2. The weather station has issued a prediction for 30% chance for rain. What is the chance that it will not rain?

3. What is 40% of 1450?

4. Find the product: $\dfrac{25}{36} \times \dfrac{27}{15} \times \dfrac{20}{33}$.

5. Find the least common multiple of 8 and 10.

Practice

Perform the indicated operations.

6. $5.88 \div 2.1$

7. $25.9 \div (-3.5)$

8. -4.3×6.3

9. $-\dfrac{6}{15} - \dfrac{3}{5}$

10. $\dfrac{6}{25} + \dfrac{7}{10}$

11. $2\dfrac{1}{8} \times 3\dfrac{3}{4}$

12. $4\dfrac{2}{5} - 2\dfrac{1}{8} + 6\dfrac{3}{10}$

13. $6.3 + 7.9 - 2.01$

14. $47 + 32 - 78$

Name _____ Date _____

Reflect & Review

1. You have a clear glass vase in the shape of a cylinder that you want to fill with sand. The cylinder is 18 inches tall and has a diameter of 4 inches. How much sand do you need? Round your answer to the nearest tenth.

2. The diameter of the Sun at its equator is 1,390,000 kilometers. Write the diameter of the Sun in scientific notation.

3. Round the decimal 625.644 to the nearest hundredth.

4. Simplify: $5 - 4(5) + 8$.

5. Find the quotient: $7\dfrac{1}{3} \div \dfrac{3}{11}$.

Practice

Find the value of the product or quotient of powers.

6. $(5)^{-3}\,(5)^4$

7. $(2)^7\,(2)^{-11}$

8. $\left(\dfrac{1}{3}\right)^5\left(\dfrac{1}{3}\right)^{-2}$

9. $\left(-\dfrac{1}{2}\right)^2\left(-\dfrac{1}{2}\right)^{-1}$

10. $\dfrac{(4)^6}{(4)^3}$

11. $\dfrac{(7)^{-1}}{(7)^2}$

12. $\dfrac{(3)^{-5}}{(3)^{-7}}$

13. $\dfrac{(-2)^4}{(4)^3}$

14. $\dfrac{(10)^3}{(10)^{-2}}$

Skills Practice

Name _____ Date _____

Reflect & Review

1. You and your family eat at a restaurant and the bill is $29.70 before tax. If the sales tax is 6%, how much do you have to pay in sales tax?

2. Kyle runs regularly at the school's track. He wants to run $3\frac{1}{2}$ miles. If one lap is $\frac{1}{4}$ of a mile, how many times will he need to run around the track?

3. Solve the equation: $6x + 12 = 8$. 4. Find the quotient: $0.54 \div 0.9$. 5. Find the value: $\left(\frac{4}{9}\right)^{-3}$

14

Practice

Write each fraction as a decimal.

6. $\frac{2}{3}$

7. $\frac{5}{6}$

8. $\frac{3}{8}$

Write the fraction that represents each repeating decimal.

9. 0.0303…

10. 0.5353…

11. 0.44…

Name _____ Date _____

1. There are 36 marbles in a bag. Fifteen of the marbles are red, 11 are blue, and 10 are green. What is the probability that you will pull a blue marble out of the bag?

2. Using information from Question 1, what is the probability of pulling a red marble and then a green marble, if you don't put the red marble back?

3. Find the slope and intercepts of the graph of $y = 4x - 8$.

14

4. Evaluate $7x - 12$ when $x = 2$.

5. Write the next three prime numbers after 13.

Decide whether each statement is true or false. Justify your decision with a complete sentence.

6. An integer is always a whole number.

7. An irrational number is sometimes a real number.

8. All integers are rational numbers.

For each problem, identify the property that is represented.

9. $4 \times 8 = 8 \times 4$

10. $\dfrac{4}{7} \times 1 = \dfrac{4}{7}$

11. $(10 + 27) + 19 = 10 + (27 + 19)$

12. $-468 + 21 = 21 + (-468)$

© 2005 Carnegie Learning, Inc.

Name _____ Date _____

1. Your quiz scores for history class so far are 87, 93, 65, 99, and 82. Find the mean, median, mode and range of the scores.

2. You are building a deck box that will fit into the corner of the deck. The shape of the box is shown.
   What is the area of the base of the deck box?

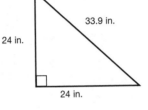

24 in. 33.9 in.

24 in.

3. Find the sum: $4\frac{1}{3} + 8\frac{1}{4} + \frac{5}{12}$.

4. Solve the proportion: $\frac{r}{8} = \frac{6}{4}$.

14

5. Write the prime factorization of 72.

Practice

Use the distributive property to evaluate each expression. Show your work.

6. $5(8 + 3)$

7. $-4(7 + 2x)$

8. $9(x + 5)$

9. $6(3x - 1)$

10. $\frac{(20 + 30)}{5}$

11. $\frac{(-15 + 12)}{-3}$

Identify the property used in each step of the equation.

12.
$$2(x - 1) + 7 = 11$$
$$2(x - 1) + 7 - 7 = 11 - 7$$
$$2(x - 1) = 4$$
$$2x - 2 = 4$$
$$2x - 2 + 2 = 4 + 2$$
$$2x = 6$$
$$\frac{2x}{2} = \frac{6}{2}$$
$$x = 3$$

Name _____ Date _____

Reflect & Review

1. Donnie is planting a row of plants along one side of his house. He is planting an area that is 12 feet long. The plants need to be 1 $\frac{1}{2}$ feet apart. How many plants will he need for the row?

2. Lexi wants a new digital camera. The camera is $130 plus tax. If the tax rate is 7%, how much will the tax on the camera be?

3. Use mental math to find the quotient: $\frac{3}{4} \div \frac{9}{16}$.

4. Solve the equation: $\frac{1}{5}x = 8$.

5. Find the sum: 23.4 + 98.7.

Practice

Graph each ordered pair on the coordinate plane. Identify the quadrant in which the point represented by the ordered pair lies.

6. (−5, 2)

7. (7, −1)

8. (−2, −3)

9. (−4, 4)

10. (−1, −6)

11. (−2, 5)

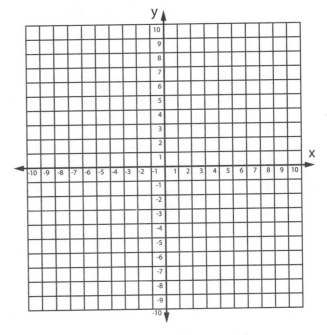

15

Skills Practice

Name _____ Date _____

Reflect & Review

1. Patty walks 2.3 miles a day, 5 days a week. How many miles does she have walk in a year?

2. Rachel's test scores for this semester are 78, 93, 89, 86 and 95. What is her average score?

3. 78 is what percent of 160?

4. Use mental math to find the product: 58×4.

5. Place the parentheses in the correct spot in order to make the statement true.

$5 + 17 - 8 \times 4 + 24 \div 7 = 41$

15

Practice

6. You are making a scale model of a statue of your school's mascot, the tiger. The actual statue is 8 feet tall. Determine the height of the model if you use a scale in which 10 feet are equal to 1 inch.

7. An action figure is 3.5 inches tall. The package that the figure came in states that a scale in which 1.75 feet are equal to 1 inch was used to create the figure. Find the height of the person that was used as a model for the action figure.

Name _____ Date _____

Reflect & Review

1. Claire wants to have an in ground hot tub. The diameter of the hot tub is 6 feet. She wants to pave 2 feet out from the edge of the hot tub. Find the area she wants to pave. Round the area to the nearest square foot.

2. Hattie works at the amusement park in the summer. She earns $7.50 per hour and receives a bonus of $50 for every 20 hours worked. How much money will she make per week if she works 23 hours?

3. Find the product: $\dfrac{6}{25} \times \dfrac{35}{48} \times \dfrac{64}{49}$

4. Simplify: $10 - 6 \times 2 + 8 \div 4$.

15

Practice

The vertices of a figure are given. Graph the figure in the coordinate plane. Then perform the indicated translation or rotation and draw the new figure.

5. Rectangle: (2, 5), (2, −1), (4, 5), (4, −1)
   Vertical translation: +3 units
   Horizontal translation: −1 unit

6. Quadrilateral: (−3, 0), (−1, −1), (1, 4), (4, 3)
   Vertical translation: −2 units
   Horizontal translation: +2 units

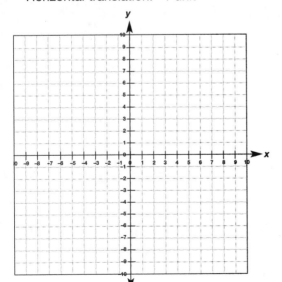

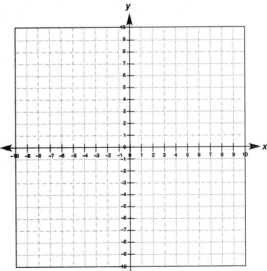

Name _____ Date _____

Reflect & Review

1. A grain silo in the shape of a cylinder is 55 feet high and has the diameter of 10 feet. Find the amount of grain the silo can hold. Round your answer to the nearest whole cubic foot.

2. If the silo in Question 1 is only 90% filled, how much grain is in the silo?

3. Use mental math to find the product: 3600 x 5.

4. Find the quotient: $\dfrac{4}{5} \div \dfrac{2}{3}$.

15

Practice

The vertices of a figure are given. Graph the figure in the coordinate plane. Then perform the indicated reflection and draw the new figure.

5. Rectangle: (1, 0), (1, 5), (6, 0), (6, 5)
Reflect figure in y-axis

6. Quadrilateral: (–2, –1), (0, –4), (6, –3), (2, –1)
Reflect figure in x-axis

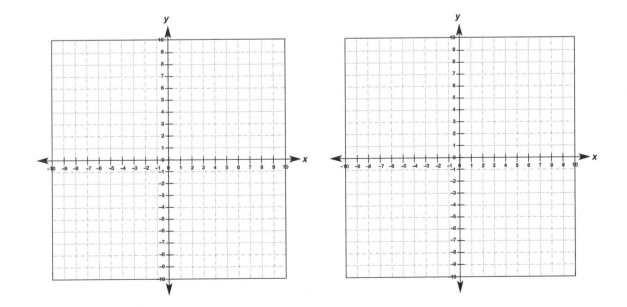

Name _____ Date _____

Reflect & Review

1. Nancy and Melissa are making brownies for the Assisted Living Center. They want to double the recipe but don't know if they have enough flour. If the original recipe requires 2 cups of flour, how much flour would be required if they double it?

2. A scientist wants to track a mouse's movements in a maze on a coordinate plane. The mouse begins at the origin and travels left 5 units, up 7 units, right 8 units and then down 3 units. Where is the mouse on the coordinate plane?

3. Find the volume of a cube with a length of 6 meters, a height of 5 meters and a width of 7 meters.

15

4. Use mental math to find the sum: $\frac{1}{4} + \frac{1}{4}$.

Practice

The vertices of a figure are given. Graph the figure in the coordinate plane. Then perform the transformations and draw the new figure.

5. Triangle: (–2, 5), (3, 0), (–4, –1)
   Vertical translation: –2 units
   Horizontal translation: +1 unit
   Reflect figure in y-axis

6. Rectangle: (6, 0), (6, –8), (2, 0), (2, –8)
   Dilate using a scale factor of 0.5
   Vertical translation: +3 units
   Horizontal translation: –2 units

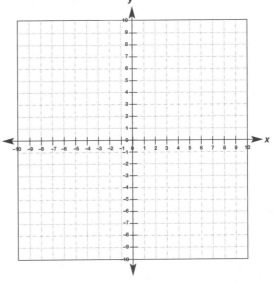